Sword
of
Pestilence

Sword
of
Pestilence

THE NEW ORLEANS
YELLOW FEVER EPIDEMIC
OF 1853

John Duffy

LOUISIANA STATE UNIVERSITY PRESS
BATON ROUGE
1966

To Moyra

whose generosity and affection
encompassed all who knew her

Preface

For a hundred years New Orleans remained the commercial center of a remote colony in the New World. The Louisiana Purchase, which made it the entrêpot for the vast Mississippi-Missouri basin, led to a rapid expansion of the city and, at the same time, profoundly altered its culture. The Americanization of New Orleans, a process which began in the late eighteenth century and gained momentum in the nineteenth, coincided with the appearance of yellow fever. The terrifying, deadly disease struck first in 1793 and did not cease its attacks until the advent of the twentieth century. For the first sixty years, 1793 to 1853, the intensity of these onslaughts seemed to correlate directly with the city's population growth. They culminated in a devastating attack in 1853, probably the worst single epidemic ever to strike a major American city. From then until 1905 the number and intensity of the epidemics tapered off; and by this time the discovery of the mosquito vector had made it possible to eradicate yellow fever. It is impossible to say precisely why yellow fever diminished after the 1850's, but certainly better drainage, screens, and the other attributes of a higher standard of living all played a part.

Although yellow fever was familiar to established residents, who seemed immune to its ravages, its etiology was unknown. And in the major outbreaks, even those who presumably had become seasoned to New Orleans occasionally fell victim to the fever. The epidemic of 1853 was a major disaster for New Orleans. Within four and a half months, a tenth of the population died and over 40 percent sickened. My immediate concern has been to show precisely what happened in the city during the disastrous summer and fall of 1853; to show how public officials, newspapers, physicians, ministers, businessmen, and others reacted in this time of crisis; and to evaluate the effect of this particular outbreak of yellow fever upon the subsequent history of New Orleans.

From a long range standpoint I believe this epidemic, coming at a time when there was a rising concern for community public health problems, helped to crystallize the southern health movement. Furthermore, it had a sharp impact upon southern medical practice. The whole field of medicine in these years was in a profound state of flux. In retrospect, it is easy to see how developments in the early nineteenth century foreshadowed the way in which bacteriology would revolutionize medicine in the last thirty years of the century. It is my opinion that the epidemic of 1853 brought the inadequacies of traditional medical practice into focus. In so doing it helped sweep away much that was useless as well as some that was positively harmful. Thus, it provided a fresh perspective and simplified the adoption of the new medical practices.

Above all, the story of this plague is a reminder that for most of recorded history mankind lived under the threat of pestilence. Only in the twentieth century have we finally eliminated the great killer diseases which periodically decimated town and countryside. Death is still with us, but his gaunt figure no longer stalks openly abroad.

If I have touched only lightly on the reactions of the poor or the impact of the disease upon the Negroes, it reflects the paucity of records. The vast majority of these individuals were inarticulate and left no permanent record of their feelings or actions. Out of necessity, I have depicted them as seen through the eyes of middle and upper class observers. For the purposes of this study, I think their collective observations were reasonably accurate.

I confess to bringing in a few extraneous items. Since my first visit to Louisiana many years ago I have been fascinated by the semitropical climate and the distinctive culture—or cultures—of the state. No picture of New Orleans at any time would be complete without some glimpses of its unique local color. My only regret is that my sense of orderliness compelled me to keep these touches to a minimum.

Acknowledgments

ONE OF THE PLEASURES of historical research and writing is that the work engenders a spirit of camaraderie among all those kindred spirits involved in the process. Historical research presents a challenge to librarians and archivists who take pride in knowing the holdings of their own institutions and in their familiarity with materials to be found elsewhere. A number of colleagues and friends who share my interest in medical history have read the manuscript and made valuable suggestions, and my research assistants and secretary have all contributed in many ways.

My research brought me into contact with staff members in a number of libraries, all of whom proved both helpful and courteous. My chief sources were found in the Louisiana State University Library, the New Orleans Public Library, the Howard-Tilton Memorial Library of Tulane University, the Rudolph Matas Medical Library, and the Louisiana State Museum Library. Among old friends in these institutions deserving of special mention are Mr. V. L. Bedsole and Miss Marcelle Schertz of the Louisiana State University Department of Archives, Miss Evangeline Lynch of the Louisiana Room in the Louisiana State University Library, Mrs. William J. Griffith of the Archives Department in Tulane University, Mrs. Rosa Oliver of the Louisiana State Museum Library, and Mr. W. D. Postell of the Rudolph Matas Medical Library. I should also like to give credit to Mr. Clive Hardie, formerly of the New Orleans Public Library, who greatly facilitated my work during the summer of 1962, and to Miss Catherine M. Brosky of the Graduate School of Public Health, University of Pittsburgh, a cheerful and efficient librarian.

My former student and colleague, Dr. Jo Ann Carrigan of Louisiana State University, whose history of yellow fever in Louisiana is ready for publication, generously shared her notes and extensive knowledge of the subject and assisted in every possible way. As usual, my chief assistant, Miss Betty Ellen Green, proved her sterling worth; and Martin Kaufman, Dorothy Thompson, Robert L. Ciaburri, Michael A. Sulman, Maurine Muncaster, and Mary V. Dobson, part-time assistants, gave strong help. My secretary, Miss Eleanor McLaughlin, proved to have an unusually sensitive ear for the English language and thus rendered service above and beyond her duties. Dr. Robert Reinders of Tulane University and Dr. Waldo L. Treuting of the University of Pittsburgh carefully read the manuscript and made valuable comments. Like most authors, I inflicted the manuscript upon my family and received particular help from my wife Corinne and my brother James.

I wish to acknowledge a special debt to Dean James A. Crabtree and Dr. Treuting of the Graduate School of Public Health, University of Pittsburgh. They provided me with ample time and research assistance. More important, the two men, by their genuine interest in history and keen intellectual curiosity, created a favorable milieu for writing. I should like, too, to thank Dr. Richard H. Shryock for his encouragement, and the American Philosophical Society for a summer travel grant which enabled me to complete the research.

JOHN DUFFY

New Orleans, Louisiana
September, 1965

Contents

Illustrations

Sword
of
Pestilence

CHAPTER I

The City That Care Forgot

THE SPRING OF 1853 was a singularly auspicious one for New Orleans. Bumper cotton crops in the South and the rapid development of the Midwest had brought prosperity to the city. The general feeling was one of buoyant optimism, although the advent of railroads was causing a few qualms among farsighted businessmen who wondered what the impact would be on the surging current of goods which annually floated down the Ohio and Mississippi rivers. From the North and from Europe capital investments were pouring into New Orleans, and with them came a flood of labor, both skilled and unskilled. From the northern states came brokers, businessmen, clerks, doctors, lawyers, boatmen, and farmers; from Germany came thousands of skilled artisans and laborers, while emigrant ships from Ireland were unloading masses of Irish peasants to supply the construction gangs engaged in draining and filling the swamps, building the roads and railways, and erecting the magnificent buildings which characterized New Orleans in its Golden Age.

With the natural levee on which the city was built extending back for only one-half mile from the river, any further expansion necessitated draining the swamps to the rear of the city. Even when drained and filled, this land was water-soaked and damp; during the many rainy spells which are common in areas along the Gulf Coast, the hovels and huts built there were often awash.

The New Orleans of the 1850's, like all other American port cities, was profoundly affected by two developments in Western Europe: the revolutions of 1848 and the Irish potato famine. The latter, which drove some two to three million people out of Ireland, brought a tremendous influx of sickly, poverty-stricken immigrants into the city. Half-starved, debilitated, and suffering from typhus and a host of other diseases, these newcomers placed a heavy burden upon the New Orleans Charity Hospital and other public and private agencies. In fact, the only significant outbreaks of typhus in Louisiana came in the years from 1847 to 1852, when destitute sick from the overcrowded emigrant vessels filled the wards and halls of the great Charity Hospital. In the years from 1850 to 1852, when admissions to the hospital ran over 18,000 per year, only about 2,000 of the patients were American-born and of these no more than 250 were native Louisianians.

The second immigrant group to come in large numbers was composed of continental Europeans, largely Germans plus a scattering of other nationality groups, some of whom were refugees from the revolutionary upheavals which swept Europe in 1848. The newcomers from the North, like the immigrants from Europe, found themselves in an environment bearing little resemblance to the homes they had left. The luxurious foliage, the heavy perfume of magnolia and oleander, the warm breeze, and the sharp, hot sunlight of semitropical New Orleans made it a world apart. The blue skies, the clouds which on a moment's notice could merge into immense thunderheads, and the Gulf downpours which periodically deluged the city and inundated the low-lying sections increased the strange appeal of New Orleans for those who had spent their early years fighting the bleak winters of New England and the northern states.

The sharp contrast between the drumming downpours of the Gulf Coast and the gentler northern rains was paralleled in society itself. The Negroes omnipresent in New Orleans streets added vivid touches to the social scene. Their careless laughter, bright clothes, languid ways, and mellifluous language made the city even more exotic. In New Orleans, where over ten thousand free Negroes lived and worked and where most of the slaves were household servants whose lot was made much more agreeable by virtue of the close personal contact between slaves and their masters, many of the worst aspects of slavery were not easily visible. To the casual observer the slave system lent an air of graciousness to life among the middle and upper classes. With an ample supply of labor for household chores, southern women were able to entertain lavishly. The management of household affairs, in which great emphasis was placed upon the social graces, was a patrician occupation rather than a never-ending task.

By 1850 the English-speaking residents far outnumbered the French, but it was the provincial French society of Louisiana which had set the pattern and tone of life in New Orleans. As it had with French Canadians, life on the frontier brought many changes to the culture of the descendants of the French who had settled in Louisiana in the eighteenth century. Yet Louisianians clung to their cultural heritage with a tenacity all the more surprising in view of the way in which their homeland had casually traded them away in 1763 and again in 1803. Forty years of Spanish dominion had altered their political and administrative institutions and had modified their way of life; nonetheless, they remained faithful to the French tradition. In this they were aided by the size of the vastly over-extended Spanish empire. The inadequate Spanish middle class and the acute shortage of professional men meant that Spain was in no position to provide either new settlers, trained administrators, or the professional classes so desperately needed in the growing colony of Louisiana. Thus Spain encouraged the importation of doctors, clergymen, and other university-trained personnel from France. Throughout the first half of the nineteenth century French-speaking New Orleanians continued to look to France for their culture and for their children's education. The revolutionary turmoils in France during these years drove many French intellectuals to Louisiana, and French language newspapers and journals flourished beside their American counterparts.

In 1853 New Orleans contained an unusually varied mixture of nationalities. Newspapers and magazines were being published in English, French, and German; and benevolent societies represented almost every national group of northwestern Europe. Adding a special touch to the city was the influence of the French Catholics. The asceticism which characterized the Irish Church had found no counterpart in Louisiana, where the Church was exceedingly liberal and understanding of human frailties. The Continental Sunday, a day of rest and recreation, outraged many staunch Puritans, and much of New Orleans' reputation for wickedness arose from the jaundiced reports of sturdy New Englanders desperately fighting losing battles with their consciences.

As a great seaport and trading mart, New Orleans inevitably had a large transient population. Thousands of sailors from all parts of the world, vast numbers of Mississippi boatmen and raftsmen, and brokers and businessmen from Europe and the northern states spent from a few days to a few months in the city. Relieved of the social pressures which would normally have inhibited them, many of the visitors frequented the less reputable establishments; and it is not to be wondered that gamblers, prostitutes, pitchmen, and a host of questionable characters were attracted to this mother lode. The slave system, too, lent itself to a double standard of morality, and whether the celebrated octoroons and quadroons of New Orleans were as beautiful and as accessible as romantically inclined writers have reported, the fact remains that they did contribute in some measure to the city's reputation. However, the lurid pictures of sexual immorality drawn by some frustrated and embittered northern writers, who, lacking personal experience with vice, were compelled to resort to imagination, are of doubtful validity. The stories about New Orleans which circulated in the mid-nineteenth century bear much resemblance to the detailed descriptions of the dens of iniquity which proved so successful in attracting crowds to revivalist camp meetings, for preachers, like writers, discovered early that the more detailed the descriptions of sin, the more appealing the message.

For all of its opulence, its opportunities for easy wealth, and its soft southern clime, New Orleans was no Garden of Eden. The oppressive summer heat and the myriad insect life drove a good share of the middle and upper classes out of the city during the long, hot, humid summers. The water table was barely a foot below the surface, there was a high summer rainfall, and mosquitoes filled the nights with their ominous humming. Malaria was endemic, but since it was a familiar disease, widespread in North America and Europe, it did not arouse the fear and consternation caused by yellow fever. This latter plague had first appeared in New Orleans at the end of the eighteenth century and had intensified its attacks as the nineteenth century wore on. Year after year epidemics of yellow fever swept through the city, killing hundreds of newly arrived residents and visitors. Unaware of the role played by mosquitoes, the medical profession and the public alike could find no logical explanation or pattern in the spread of this horrible disease. On some occasions it appeared to be imported, on others to spring up spontaneously. Often the yellow fever victim brought sickness to his entire household; at other times not another member of the family was touched by the disease.

Like most cities during the first half of the nineteenth century, New Orleans lacked the machinery for collecting vital statistics—a fact which left municipal authorities completely untroubled. Prominent doctors, newspaper editors, and civic leaders were convinced that their city was a veritable health spa. True, they admitted, yellow fever and other diseases exacted a heavy toll, but these fatalities occurred almost exclusively among the ignorant and dissolute poor. Once a newcomer had passed through the "seasoning" or acclimating process, he would then be virtually immune to the epidemic diseases. Moreover, even newcomers could protect themselves by leaving the city in June and not returning until the frosts had ended all danger from the epidemic fevers of summer. For those who had no choice but to stay through the yellow fever season, little danger was to be expected so long as the individual lived a life of moderation and procured sound medical care immediately at the onset of any indisposition. Occasional "troublemakers" raised objections to these happy assumptions, but their voices were soon silenced. In 1849 and 1850, however, several leading physicians had investigated the situation and discovered that New Orleans was the very antithesis of a health resort.[1] Their findings were given wide publicity and temporarily jarred the city out of its complacency. But unpleasant facts are soon forgotten; by 1853 the newspapers were once again proclaiming the virtues of the city's site and climate.

The attacks of yellow fever which gave New Orleans its reputation as a pesthole occurred almost every summer, and periodically the disease flared up into serious proportions. In twelve of the thirty-five years from 1825 to 1860, the annual death toll exceeded 1,000, and the rapid growth of the city's population provided more and more fuel for this raging pestilence. Between 1837 and 1843 each of four epidemics swept away from 1,500 to 2,000 persons, while still another epidemic, in 1847, killed 2,700. The recurrent and intensifying outbreaks during these years were but a prelude to the explosive outbursts of yellow fever which devastated New Orleans in the 1850's.[2]

Following the serious epidemic of 1847, the tide of fever sullenly receded from New Orleans. When less than 900 yellow fever deaths occurred in the summers of 1848 and 1849, a feeling of relief swept through the population, and cautious hopes were expressed that the worst might be over. The next two summers saw only a few scattered cases, changing the earlier cautious hopes into optimistic assertions. In 1852 the death toll jumped to about 450, but this merely confirmed the assumption that the disease was on the wane. The prevailing attitude was expressed in the city directory for 1853. In praising the work of Mayor A. D. Crossman, the editor wrote: "Five consecutive summers have now elapsed, since the scourge, which has made the name of our city a synonym for Lazaar house, . . . appeared in an epidemic form. Yellow Fever in New Orleans is now considered by the faculty an 'obsolete idea'." [3]

The winter of 1852–53 had been particularly successful for New Orleans. Some 130 million dollars worth of produce had found its way down the Mississippi for distribution from the city, leaving in its wake general prosperity for all concerned. A strong demand and ample shipping had enabled businessmen to clear the wharves and warehouses earlier than usual, and permitted many of them to close their accounts and leave their clerks and warehousemen in charge. The result was that the general flight at the beginning of summer to the resort areas of the north and the Gulf Coast started earlier than usual. Early in May of 1853, the city began settling down into the warm-weather doldrums. The mass summer exodus was not yet complete, but social life was slowing down as the sun lengthened its diurnal journey and each day saw the temperature creep up a degree or so. For those with money and leisure, there were still plenty of amusements available. On Monday night, May 2, the Orleans Theatre presented Rossini's opera, *Moses in Egypt*; on Thursday the same company offered Mozart's *Don Giovanni*. On Tuesday, for those who preferred a more varied evening's entertainment, Placides Varieties provided a program to suit everybody's taste: Shakespeare's *King Lear*, dances by Mlle. Ducy Barre, and to top off the evening's performance, a farce entitled *Betsy Baker*.[4] Over at the Southern Museum, described as one of the most pleasant resorts of the city, such popular plays as the *Golden Farmer* and that "Grand Domestic Drama . . . 'The Drunkard' " were playing to near-capacity audiences.[5] Life in the rest of the city was going along much as usual. Routine matters preoccupied the local courts; for example, cabaret-owner R. Jones was fined ten dollars for selling liquor to slaves. In another case, a fine was imposed on David King, free man of color, for permitting an illegal assembly of slaves in his cabaret; the two slaves who constituted the illegal assembly were given twenty-five lashes apiece. A coroner's inquest over the body of a slave girl pronounced that her sudden death had resulted from that classic complaint of earlier years, "inflamation of the bowels." [6]

As the heat started reacting upon the garbage, offal, and sewage which floated in the gutters, drainage ditches, canals, and open pools, indignant citizens began protesting to the city fathers. On Wednesday night, May 4, the aldermen hotly debated the issue at their weekly meeting. Accusations of neglect of duty were hurled against the street commissioner, and after much discussion the aldermen resolved to investigate the matter and, if the evidence warranted it, to bring charges of impeachment against him.[7] Over and above the aesthetic considerations, a few physicians had been fighting for sanitary reform for many years. Dr. Abner Hester, editor of the *New Orleans Medical & Surgical Journal*, in the May, 1853, issue had urged that provision be made for "a plentiful supply of water for the purpose of cleaning the gutters." When the city had achieved this happy state, Dr. Hester wrote, "we may hope to see our annual bill of mortality compare more favorably with those of other cities than it does now." He reminded his readers of the assertion by Dr. Benjamin Rush, the famous American physician of an earlier generation, that civic authorities should be held accountable for the lives of all who died of preventable diseases within their cities. "How many of our honorable councilmen," he asked, "have ever considered the subject in this view?" [8]

Although he had issued a warning to the municipal officials, Dr. Hester was well satisfied with the existing state of health in New Orleans. In the March, 1853, issue of his *Journal* he had written: "We cannot recall a single corresponding season during which we have seen and heard of less serious sickness." Noting that only 1,218 deaths had occurred in the past nine weeks, he concluded happily, "When we regard the immense population now in New Orleans, both floating and permanent, we are no less surprised than gratified at the sanitary condition to which our city has attained." [9] The following month he commented that the city "has been blessed with extraordinary health. . . ." The "late mortality from *Fevers*," he said, "has been uncommonly small," a fact which he attributed to the "very little *Ship Fever*" (typhus) brought in by the emigrants from Europe. Most of these newcomers who arrived during the winter and spring "were in very good condition." The spring had arrived quite late, he added, with the result that very few mosquitoes had appeared as of the middle of April. Taking note of the connection which had been suggested between mosquitoes and yellow fever, he commented: "The relation that this fact may bear to the state of health both now and hereafter will be worthy of notice, as the elements that enter into their generation may be intimately connected with *morbific causes*." [10] Ironically, the cool and pleasant spring of 1853, with its freedom from mosquitoes and other insects, gave little hint of what lay in store for New Orleans in the coming months.

As the pleasant days of May wore on, there appeared little to dim the bright prospects of the city. Reports from the New Orleans Charity Hospital showed fewer admissions and deaths than usual, but there were a few more cases of remittent fever than normal, a fact which was attributed to the extensive clearing and partial drainage of the swamp as the city pushed out from the river. The contemporary explanation for malaria, and also the other epidemic fevers, was the miasmatic theory. According to this thesis, a gaseous substance was emitted by putrid and decaying vegetation which, under certain circumstances, caused the classic bouts of alternate chills and fever characteristic of malaria ("bad air"), or fever and ague, as it was generally known. A variation on this theme emphasized the heat of the sun upon newly drained land as an intensifying factor. In previous yellow fever epidemics, there had been indignant outcries against draining the swamps, but for several years the work had progressed with no evident deleterious results. Most of the newspapers favored expanding the city in the direction of Lake Pontchartrain and hence tended to discount any danger from draining the low-lying areas during the hot months. Moreover, their concern was primarily with economic matters—only when epidemics or other forms of sickness threatened trade and commerce did the newspapers take a firm stand. The *Bee*, in both its French and English issues, staunchly advocated expanding the city limits into the swampy areas and making the city a leading railroad center. In the spring of 1853 every omen seemed favorable, and on May 19, the editor proclaimed: "The influence of enterprize has already secured to New Orleans a future so glorious, that imagination can scarcely conceive a more brilliant destiny. The herald of that epoch of unsurpassed prosperity and greatness has already appeared. We behold the earnest of the coming day in the growing population and increasing wealth of the city. . . ." [11] By continuing steadily and purposefully on her present path, he said, New Orleans was certain of becoming "the Imperial City of the South." [12] Ten days later the editor of the *Daily Picayune* sought to outdo the *Bee* in predicting a glorious future for the city. Although it possessed more natural advantages than any population center in the world, he asserted, New Orleans had failed to use them effectively. Now that she had awakened to a recognition that "Nature has placed no limits to her greatness, she must become one of the largest cities in the world, perhaps one day the greatest commercial emporium on the face of the earth." [13] On these happy notes the bright month of May drew to a close.

To some members of the medical profession, however, events in Charity Hospital toward the end of the month struck a disharmonious chord. On May 27 an Irish laborer recently landed from an emigrant vessel was admitted suffering from the black vomit and died a few hours later. The patient had been placed in a ward of Dr. Erasmus Darwin Fenner, a leading southern physician, an outstanding medical editor and writer, and a man of strong, forthright opinions. Fenner, who was considered an authority on southern diseases and particularly yellow fever, was quite worried by the existence of what appeared to be the fever at such an early date. A classic case with high temperature, jaundice, intestinal hemorrhages, and vomiting (the so-called black vomit was a regurgitation of partially digested blood) was not too hard to diagnose at a time when the disease was widespread, but these cases rarely appeared at the beginning of outbreaks. The early physicians, entirely dependent upon the observation of clinical signs and symptoms, learned their art well in the school of experience, and many were master diagnosticians; even so, differentiating between hemorrhagic malaria, yellow fever, and one or two other contagions was no simple task. Furthermore, a diagnosis of yellow fever in New Orleans was not to be made lightly. Almost invariably, a physician identifying an early case as yellow fever found himself denounced for needlessly arousing public apprehension. Not only the municipal officers and newspaper editors, but even his colleagues, were likely to question the diagnosis. It behooved the doctor, then, to be absolutely certain—and preferably to have the support of one or two of his colleagues—before declaring the presence of yellow fever.

After the death of his patient with black vomit and the discovery of another case resembling yellow fever, Dr. Fenner, who on earlier occasions had sought to trace the origins of epidemics, resolved to investigate the background of these cases. He felt, he wrote later, "that if the facts and circumstances were not then ascertained, it would be vain to search for them after the lapse of even a few months." [14] He concluded that the first cases had occurred on the ship *Augusta*, which had arrived direct from Bremen on May 17, carrying 230 European immigrants. The trip had been an unusually healthy one, with only 2 children dying of diarrhea en route. The only possible source of contamination had been a close contact with another vessel, the *Camboden Castle*, on the long trip up the Mississippi to New Orleans. This latter ship, according to the captain, whom Dr. Fenner interviewed at the end of May, had lost its previous master and several crew members from yellow fever while in Kingston, Jamaica. Subsequently it had sailed for New Orleans and had had no further sickness.[15]

The yellow fever cases on the *Augusta* had been attended by Dr. Moritz Schuppert, a well-known New Orleans physician. Dr. Schuppert was called aboard the vessel on May 23 to treat a twenty-one-year-old sailor suffering from what Schuppert thought was gastroduodenitis. The symptoms were a pulse rate of 100, hot dry skin, violent headache, pains in the back and limbs, coated tongue, foul-smelling breath, with nausea and the vomiting of "bilious matters." On the fifth day the sick man's skin and eyes turned yellow, but recovery followed in a few days. On May 25 a second sailor became ill, with similar but more violent symptoms; he died on May 30 in a state of delirium. On the twenty-seventh of May two more sailors exhibited identical symptoms; one recovered, but the other died on May 30. Dr. Schuppert was able to secure a postmortem and noted that the body was quite yellow and the stomach contained "about two ounces of black vomit." A fifth victim from the ship took sick on May 30 and died in Charity Hospital on June 7. In commenting upon these cases, Dr. Fenner noted that he found his colleagues in considerable dispute as to the nature of the disease, but asserted that he personally was convinced that the men had died of yellow fever.[16]

As the sickness was spreading among the crew of the *Augusta*, a butcher living fourteen blocks away from the wharf where the ship was anchored became ill with a disease almost identical to that of the sailors. After vomiting "a large quantity of black matters" he subsequently recovered. In his case, too, the doctors were undecided about the diagnosis. Meanwhile, a number of other cases began appearing in Charity Hospital. James McGuigan, an Irish immigrant engaged in unloading a ship anchored near the *Augusta*, was admitted to the hospital on May 27 and died on the morning of May 28. At the postmortem, held under the direction of Dr. Fenner, but with five or six other physicians in attendance, all agreed on a diagnosis of yellow fever.[17] Although the evidence seemed to point to the waterfront as the place of origin, Dr. M. M. Dowler, another able physician, was called upon to treat two cases of unmistakable yellow fever in the low-lying swampy section to the rear of the city. The two patients, a German immigrant who worked in the swamp and his wife, were questioned by Dowler but insisted that they had never visited the waterfront. Subsequently they both succumbed to the disease.[18] The opening days of June saw the number of cases begin to increase, but the pattern which emerged throws little light on the place of origin. In 1853 New Orleans physicians, like those in other areas plagued by yellow fever, were still desperately seeking a logical explanation for the cause of the disease.

Medicine was primarily concerned with the problem of the great epidemic diseases. As the scientific advances of the eighteenth and nineteenth centuries unlocked more of the secrets of nature and provided an ever-increasing number of clues to the causal factors of sickness and disease, intelligent physicians and laymen frantically sought everywhere for additional pieces of information. Meteorological and geographical conditions, for example, were examined in an effort to discover any correlations with the prevailing sicknesses. As it became evident that the old theories of medical practice no longer had validity, a host of new ones or modifications of old ones proliferated.

The significant developments in mathematics and the emergence of basic laws in astronomy during the seventeenth century had convinced the intellectuals of the eighteenth and early nineteenth centuries that just as Newton's law of gravitation had explained the mechanics of the universe, so man, by the power of his intellect, could find the one fundamental law of health. The age-old search for a panacea found justification with the age of rationalism. Thus it was that Benjamin Rush's concept of the unity of fevers, the idea that diseases were merely different forms of the same fever, found such widespread acceptance in the early ninetenth century. Ironically, the emergence of clinical or hospital medicine and the development of the biological and physical sciences, which were soon to change the nature of medicine, merely accelerated the multiplication of medical theories. Certainly, in the case of yellow fever, the 1850's saw physicians attributing the disease to a multitude of diverse causes and saw patients treated in as many different ways. It was for these reasons that Fenner, Schuppert, and Dowler were so zealous in gathering every shred of evidence relating to the origins of the epidemic, hoping that a pattern would emerge which would provide some insight into the cause and control of this scourge. Although the data collected were to be of value to future researchers, they provided no clues for Dr. Fenner and his colleagues.

CHAPTER II

Sporadic or Epidemic?

Whatever may have been the apprehensions of a few of the "medical gentlemen," with respect to yellow fever that late spring of 1853, they were not shared by the citizens in general. June proved to be relatively uneventful. The weather was hot and a little drier than usual; economic activity was undergoing the customary summer slow down; and a good share of the so-called "better people" were boarding the steamboats and trains for summer resorts in the North and along the Gulf Coast. The City Council, also known as the Common Council, continued to hold its regular weekly meetings to deal with routine matters and to take cognizance of occasional protests from individual constituents.

The sessions, as was to be expected, were enlivened now and then by heated arguments and personal clashes. The last meeting in May, for example, saw a violent exchange between one of the assistant aldermen, Henry Guyol, and the keeper of the city prison, a Mr. Beauregard, who accused Guyol of lying. The latter, outraged at this imputation upon his honor, immediately seized an inkstand and hurled it at his adversary. Not to be outdone, Beauregard, as the newspaper account stated, "returned a similar missile, and for a time great confusion prevailed in the Board." Fortunately the other council members were able to separate the two combatants, and when tempers cooled, apologies were exchanged.[1] As frequently happens, the only sufferers in the fracas were two innocent bystanders. One of these, a Mr. S. Davis presented a petition at the next meeting of the council claiming that while quietly listening to the city fathers debate civic matters, "he was rudely and unprovokedly assailed by an inkstand." This missile, he wrote, had passed within a few inches of his head and "struck the body of an Irish gentleman in his rear," bespattering his own clothing as it fell. He requested compensation for the damage to his clothes; under the circumstances, the council felt it had no alternative but to pay. The Irish gentleman, from whom nothing was heard, apparently accepted his injuries as one of the normal hazards associated with attendance at council meetings.[2]

The public was probably more concerned with the details of a rather sensational murder trial then underway. A Miss Agnes Anderson had been under indictment for the murder of her lover William B. Taylor; public sympathy, aroused by a series of human-interest newspaper stories on the defendant, was solidly on the young lady's side. According to her testimony, the victim had seduced her by a promise of marriage and then refused to save her honor. In utter despair, and carried away by the realization that her life was completely ruined, she had gone to his room and proceeded to stab him to death with a clasp knife. Long before the opening of the court session every corridor leading to the room was jammed, and a minute or two after the doors were opened, every seat was taken. Conscious of its obligation both to southern womanhood and American motherhood, the jury took but five minutes to reach its decision of acquittal.[3]

The most exciting event of the month occurred in the middle of June, when rumors of a great slave rebellion swept through the city. After forceful interrogation of several slaves and free Negroes, the police issued guns and mobilized all their men. A battalion of artillery was called out, and armed men began patrolling the streets with orders to arrest Negroes on sight. These precautions proved needless; after making several arrests, the police conceded that the whole thing had been a false alarm. But the incident received a good deal of newspaper publicity.

While the city went about its customary business, a few isolated news items in the daily papers foreshadowed coming events. On June 1 a brief story taken from a New York newspaper was published, stating that yellow fever was prevalent in Jamaica and making heavy inroads among the sailors and dock workers; but Jamaica was a long way from New Orleans, and yellow fever was to be expected in the West Indies.[4] On June 7 a more disquieting piece of news was tucked away in small print under the heading "Local Affairs." The editor explained that by accident a report from the Charity Hospital had appeared in the preceding issue stating that two cases of black vomit had appeared in the hospital. This fact, the editor said, "isolated and without explanation, is too well calculated to produce a wrong impression both here and abroad." The two victims, he said, had caught the disease in Havana and fallen sick in New Orleans, something which often happened in New York, Boston, and Philadelphia and was certainly no cause for alarm. "And everybody knows, or ought to know," he went on confidently, "that this kind of disease is not imported. New Orleans, if we examine carefully the statistics, is *per se*, one of the healthiest cities of the Union." Evidently having paid little attention to the statistics gathered shortly before by several leading physicians showing a very different picture, the editor proclaimed: "We have suffered, as a city, enough already from traditional vileness and bug-bear stories, and it is about time we looked carefully to our reports, so that nothing calculated to mislead persons abroad or citizens at home, should have publicity." [5]

This inverted logic which assumed that publishing the truth about yellow fever cases was misleading and that carefully avoiding all mention of the presence of the disease served the cause of justice was by no means unique to New Orleans. Throughout the eighteenth and nineteenth centuries American newspapers assiduously culled out from their columns all references to the local presence of epidemic diseases until the news could no longer be concealed. The standard procedure—and the first evidence of an approaching outbreak—was for the local journals indignantly to deny the false rumors; when the death toll soared and a mass exodus got underway, the newspapers then fell discreetly silent until the worst was over. At this time, they would begin issuing statements, usually premature, asserting that the outbreak was now over and that those who had left could safely return to the city.

With the exception of a few perceptive individuals, the public and the medical profession alike paid little attention to the portents of the coming storm. On June 17 the *Delta* published a humorous account of a meeting of the "Stay-at-Home Club," a group of businessmen who were compelled to spend the long, hot summer in New Orleans. The following day the paper with tongue in cheek apologized for not giving the group its correct name, the "Can't-Get-Away-Club." [6] About this time stories began appearing in all the papers about the exceedingly hot weather. On June 22 the editor of the *Daily Crescent* consoled members of the "Can't-Get-Away Club" with the thought that the discomforts of summer were "more fanciful than real." He pointed out that the city's commercial growth required merchants and businessmen to stay on the job far more than they had in the past. Suggesting that summer vacation trips be shortened, he declared: "Now that yellow fever has become an obsolete idea in New Orleans, there can be no longer an excuse for our citizens remaining from home in the early fall." [7]

Two days later the same newspaper noted that "the yearly stampede [was] nearly over," and that the city was settling down into its summer lassitude. Although things were dull, life would be quite pleasant were it not for "the buzzing and biting of the mosquitoes. . . ." Even the mosquitoes were not without some consolation, the paper added, since ladies were willing to permit gentlemen to smoke in their presence as a means of keeping away the ubiquitous insects. [8] Within a few days the mosquito hordes literally began taking over the city. A semihumorous editorial declared that the major question was whether to kill the mosquitoes or to be killed by them. "A barbarous horde of great, ugly, long billed, long legged, fly away creatures has invaded our streets and houses, and taken possession of our domestic goods," the editorial continued, adding that the "burning of tobacco or powdered rosin, or brown paper" was all to no avail. [9]

A few days later the *Delta*, too, felt compelled to editorialize upon the mosquito scourge. Never had they been so bad, the editor commented. Apropos the subject of yellow fever which had been raised by "some of our weak-kneed brothers," the editorial questioned whether Providence would send two curses at once—yellow fever and mosquitoes. In any event, it confidently concluded, "Yellow Fever, it is settled, is curable—quite manageable by medical skill," whereas no remedy existed for the mosquitoes! [10]

As the summer closed in on New Orleans and the citizenry doggedly settled down to the prospect of three months of oppressive heat, the cheerful comments about warm weather gradually disappeared from the newspapers. The *Delta* made one final effort on June 30 when the editor wrote: "Yet, after all, this is the proper weather for New Orleans. It is always healthiest when it is hottest. It is your damp, changeable, coolish weather, which creates sickness, and disturbs the healthy operation of the physical system." [11] Surprisingly, in view of the plethora of mosquitoes in New Orleans, the June weather was generally hot and dry throughout the state. In fact, the cool, moist spring had proved no augury of the summer weather. From St. Mary Parish a report described the health of the area as excellent, the crops fine, the weather hot, dry, and dusty, and the nights clear, but "close and oppressive." From Shreveport the news was essentially the same, with the added notation that the hot weather was very helpful to the cotton and corn. From Ouachita

Parish the report was that the cotton crop was thinning but that the planters were becoming apprehensive over the possibility of drought. Baton Rouge, which was too close to the Gulf to grow cotton and corn, reported that its crops desperately needed rain.[12] Although a few apprehensions were expressed about the long dry spell, optimistic health reports came from every area of the state, a fact which tended to confirm the general impression in New Orleans that the city would once again escape Yellow Jack.

Although the first hot days in May usually brought demands in New Orleans for a sanitary program to remove the dirt and filth putrefying in the streets, on the levees, and on private property, it was not until June that the rising crescendo of indignant outcries led to any effective measures. New Orleans was not unique in this respect. No city in the mid-nineteenth century had faced up to the growing problems of urbanism, and such sewage and sanitary facilities as existed were hopelessly inadequate. The strong spirit of individualism and the universal distrust of government at all levels precluded any really effective reform; and, even where a few tentative steps were taken, the mushrooming of the cities soon nullified any beneficial results.

In June a complicating factor usually was added to the already problematic health conditions. With good reason, early Americans entertained a healthy fear of rabies. Coming from rural backgrounds, most of them considered a dog a dog, a domesticated animal who earned his keep. Although many were household pets, given consideration as members of the family, for the most part they lived a dog's life. Sensitivity to the sufferings of animals was only beginning, and few individuals had any compunctions about turning a dog loose on the streets when he was no longer needed or wanted. The net effect was that packs of dogs roamed the streets, competing with the hogs as scavengers; and as long as they committed no depredations upon the hogs or the residents, they were ordinarily left alone. With the advent of June and what was considered the rabies season, however, the matter was seen in a new light, and it was a standard practice for the police to distribute poisoned sausages as a means of eliminating stray dogs. The citizens usually were warned beforehand to keep their dogs leashed or fastened in their yards. The street-cleaning contractors were responsible for removing the dead bodies of poisoned animals, but in this they were no more diligent than in their other duties; the result was that the putrefying bodies of dead dogs accentuated the foul miasmas arising from the gutters and sinkholes. Hence it was no coincidence that a week after the New Orleans

Board of Assistant Aldermen had instructed "the Street Commissioner to distribute poisoned sausages on the streets for dogs," the same body should order the police to enforce all ordinances relating to the presence of obstructions and animals in the city streets.[13]

As early as the eighteenth century, American towns had established agencies for cleaning the streets and emptying the privies of what was delicately referred to as "night soil." For the most part these services were performed by private contractors; as long as the towns remained small and these people could be held personally responsible, the system worked more or less effectively. As cities grew like Topsy in the nineteenth century and political democracy broadened the base for corruption, the street-cleaning contracts became prize political plums, and it was understood that the contractors would perform only nominal duties. Periodically—usually under the threat of an approaching epidemic sickness or in the face of a serious outbreak—the public would demand that they live up to their contracts, and proposals would be made to substitute a permanent force of city employees in the place of private contractors. Fortunately for the contractors, public memory was short; once the crisis ended, the established ineffective methods quickly regained sway.

Mayor Crossman of New Orleans, an able and conscientious official, had no illusions about the contract system. On June 14 he drew the attention of the Board of Aldermen to the filthy state of the streets and gutters, laid the blame on the private contractors, and urged that the city hire its own street-cleaning force. He sent a similar message to the Board of Assistant Aldermen, who also received at the same time a communication from the street commissioner explaining his inability to cope with the situation because of limited personnel and "the dilatoriness of the contractors for cleaning the streets." [14] When the assistant aldermen met a week later, they took note of petitions coming from several areas protesting the filthy condition of the streets. One of these, from the residents of Bourbon Street, claimed that offal was being thrown into an alley after the cleaners' carts had passed. In response, the board officially rebuked the street commissioner for negligence. Another petition from the residents of Common Street protested "against the proprietors of the St. Charles, Verandah, & City Hotels being permitted to empty their privies into the street." Since these three were the largest hotels in the city, the matter was referred to the alderman from the Third Ward who was to report at the next meeting.[15]

The existence of these petitions and the demands for action on the part of the mayor were not at all unusual. What is surprising, however, is the speed with which the members of the City Council reacted to the mayor's plea. On June 21 the Board of Assistant Aldermen unanimously resolved that the street commissioner be instructed to hire men to clean and repair the streets and to deduct the costs from the amount paid to the street contractors in whose district the work was performed.[16] The need for such action was made even more evident on June 28 when Street Commissioner James Jolls reported that not one of the contractors was performing his duties and that it appeared the only way to get the streets clean was for the city to hire its own men. He informed the council, too, that he had sent some men to clean up the old Vegetable Market at Tchoupitoulas and Annunciation streets which had become "an intolerable nuisance," and that the workers "could hardly stand the stench arising therefrom." [17]

Meeting the same night, June 28, the Committee on Streets and Landings reported to the Board of Aldermen that it approved the mayor's suggestion for abolishing the contract system and recommended that the existing street-cleaning contracts not be renewed upon their expiration. The aldermen accepted the committee's report and resolved that plans be drawn for establishing a municipal street-cleaning department. The aldermen also concurred in the assistant aldermen's resolution to prosecute delinquent contractors and to cancel agreements with those fined three successive times within one month. Both boards further agreed to a resolution calling for the election of a superintendent of carts and laborers.[18]

On the surface, there is little to be found in the newspapers, journals, and minutes of the City Council to indicate why officials should have decided so quickly to scrap the ancient and time-honored system of private street contractors simply because the streets were malodorous and dirty. It is doubtful that they were any worse than they had been in previous years or even much worse than they were to become in some of the future years. Logically something must have bestirred the councilmen out of their customary lethargy, and the answer probably lies in the lurking suspicion that yellow fever was threatening the Crescent City. On June 23 the *Picayune* gave some hint of this possibility when it published a letter to the editor under the caption "Yellow Fever Alarm." An editorial note stated that the correspondent, who simply signed himself "Observer," could "be relied on as good authority." The writer began by asserting: "Madam Rumor has given rise to the fancied existence of yellow fever in this city to a very great extent." He conceded that four cases had occurred, but "that it exists in a form or to an extent to produce alarm, except amongst old women," he went on, "is most positively denied by all the most eminent physicians in the city." He noted that weekly lists of deaths had been published "under the sanction of a *Board of Health*," and he demanded to know if such a board existed and if so, by whose authority. These unfortunate reports, he declared, had induced many citizens "to leave the city sooner than convenient in order to avoid a danger which does not exist." [19] Just previously another paper published a letter from "Anti-Yellow Fever," who gave a humorous account of his meeting with Death. Death, according to this correspondent, had wanted to go north, but the actions of the City Council and the accumulating filth in the city had compelled him to remain in New Orleans.[20] On June 24 the *Picayune* published a short note beginning: "We found on our table last evening the following list of interments in this city for week ending June 18, 1853." The list, which was signed by Dr. Abner Hester, secretary of the Board of Health, included seven deaths from yellow fever. The editor added the following comment: "The doctors of our city appear to be in difficulty as to whether there is, or is not, a Board of Health here. Some say there is, and some as positively assert that there is not. This is an important matter, and we should like to know, and so would the public, the truth of the whole affair." [21] Two days later the *Delta* published a report from Charity Hospital indicating that 643 patients were suffering from fever, principally "of the intermittent or bilious kind." [22] Although a sifting of evidence clearly shows that yellow fever cases and deaths were steadily increasing, no mention of this fact was made. It is evident that the newspapers and civic leaders had become aware of the possible danger; but, partially in response to economic pressure and possibly in part because of a subconscious wish to suppress an unpleasant truth, they were resolved to deny the existence of any threat to public safety.

Whatever may have been the public position of the leading citizens, it is obvious that a second exodus was underway in the closing days of June. Although six years had elapsed since the last major epidemic, yellow fever was a terrible disease and the memories of its repeated attacks on New Orleans were still fresh. Even newcomers to the city must have had qualms, since on their arrival they were certain to have been informed of their special susceptibility. Despite the official silence, news of black vomit cases must have spread very rapidly by word of mouth, and the newspaper denials may only have served to quicken fears and increase anxieties.

The concern of the City Council at this time becomes even clearer in the light of its actions with respect to the Board of Health. Throughout the previous fifty years, New Orleans had seen a number of health boards come and go. Each successive yellow fever or Asiatic cholera epidemic gave rise to demands for an effective board, but public apathy on one hand and the active opposition of a small minority on the other had helped undermine the early health agencies. The quarantine issue—whether or not yellow fever could be kept out of New Orleans by rigid examination of incoming ships—was still a major divisive force among those who conscientiously sought public health reform; it had helped destroy some of the earlier boards and, for many years to come, was to prove the rock upon which other health boards would founder. Theoretically New Orleans in 1853 had an effective Board of Health, one provided with extensive powers. Its legal basis was an act of 1848 of the Louisiana Legislature which authorized the city to appoint a 12-man board with wide supervisory authority. Two years later the membership was increased to fifteen and the board was authorized to hire health wardens, impose fines on street-cleaning contractors for neglect of duty, require death certificates from physicians, and make various regulations with respect to the city's health.[23]

In actual fact this health board had little real authority. In the first place the members were appointed for a limited time only. Each May the City Council elected new board members whose tenure of office ran only until the following December. Thus from the beginning it was assumed that the health officers functioned solely during the sickly summer months and that their services were really needed only in times of major epidemics. As early as 1850 the Board of Health had presented a discouraging picture of its role: physicians had refused to cooperate in recording burial certificates; lack of funds had prevented the hiring of health wardens; the regulations with respect to cleaning the streets had proved unenforceable; and the board had found its function to be purely advisory—but, alas, even this latter function was illusory since, the board's Annual Report noted, no one bothered to heed its advice!

Compounding the troubles of the Board of Health were the current theories of epidemiology. In 1848, for example, board members had been criticized for failing to declare the existence of a yellow fever epidemic despite the board's own reports which showed a total of 1,195 cases and 716 deaths from yellow fever. In response to this criticism, the members explained that their policy was not to proclaim an epidemic unless the number of cases of yellow fever was rising rapidly while the incidence of intermittent fever was dropping sharply. Since there had been more cases of intermittent fever than yellow fever in the summer of 1848, the board members felt that yellow fever was sporadic and not epidemic. Closely allied with this concept was another current idea that a disease could not be considered epidemic until the number of deaths from it equalled, or exceeded, the total deaths from all other causes. The net effect of this inability to define what constituted an epidemic was to bring the health board under criticism from all sides. A virtual tidal wave of opposition was aroused among the newspapers and in the business community whenever the board had the temerity to report the first few yellow fever cases; and if the disease got out of control, these same groups had no compunctions about turning around and accusing the board of failing to do its duty. To add to the board's woes, the few conscientious medical men who fought for sanitary and quarantine reforms invariably felt that the Board of Health was too weak and ineffectual to deserve support.

Early in 1852 the Louisiana Legislature, in reorganizing the city government of New Orleans, failed to provide for a board of health. Apparently the omission aroused no great outcry since the opponents of the board were delighted to be rid of it, and its proponents were devoutly hoping that the way was now clear for creating an effective body. In the spring of 1852 Dr. A. Forster Axson, editor of the *New Orleans Monthly Medical Register*, a relatively new publication, urged the City Council not to "revive our old and exploded contrivance of a Board of Health." Although its members had legislated "with wisdom and propriety," he said, its authority had been "scoffed at in the four quarters of the city, its officers defied, and its advice respected as a piece of gratuity, for which no one was obliged." [24] Despite criticism from all sides, in May of 1852 the City Council, acting on its own authority, reestablished a new board of health similar to its unlamented predecessor. Precisely what happened to this board is difficult to say. No evidence exists to show that it took any action or even made any recommendations. According to one of the New Orleans newspapers, the board members were so disgusted with the failure of all responsible authorities in the city to cooperate with them that they adjourned *sine die*, leaving their secretary, Dr. Abner Hester, as the sole representative. [25] It was Dr. Hester, however, who aroused the ire of the newspapermen by faithfully reporting the growing number of deaths from yellow fever in June of 1853. Although the daily papers carefully avoided publishing these reports—except for an oversight by the *Picayune* when it printed the mortality figures for the week ending June 18—yellow fever deaths as early as the month of June could scarcely have been kept quiet.

It was this background, undoubtedly, which led the Board of Aldermen on June 28 to appoint a committee of three to confer with the assistant aldermen on the matter of creating a Board of Health. In their resolution the aldermen noted that they had already resolved to establish a board on March 8 but that the assistant aldermen had rejected the proposal. Suffice it to say, the assistant aldermen quickly appointed a conference committee on June 30, and negotiations got underway. With each board jealous of its authority, almost a month elapsed before a health board officially came into existence.[26]

In the meantime public attention was centered upon a duel which occurred between two immigrants, the editors of New Orleans' two German newspapers. The duel excited angry comment by at least one newspaper regarding the inhumanity of the practice of settling arguments by dueling.[27]

The City Council, at this time, was concerned with more practical problems. Spurred on by shocked expressions from the respectable elements in the city, on June 23 the following ordinance was passed: "*Be it ordained*, That all persons are forbidden to bathe in the river or ponds in front of this town, or in the ponds or ditches in any part of the town; and all are forbidden to strip or expose their naked person or body in any part of the town, on the bank of the river or in the river or ponds." A fine of $5 was to be imposed for such offenses, but the ordinance was qualified by the provision that it did not apply to individuals bathing "after dark or during the night time." [28] An even more vital question, which invariably came up about this time of year, was the proper mode for the city to celebrate the Glorious Fourth. In their usual fashion, the two boards disputed over the amount of money which should be appropriated for this purpose, but concurred in voting $100 for each of the city's orphan asylums.[29] At the same meeting the councilmen referred to the police committee a suggestion that the council fix limits "within which houses of ill-fame are to be allowed." [30] The tendency of the bordellos to stray into respectable neighborhoods, it seemed, was causing considerable discomfort to the residents and complicating the efforts of the police force to maintain law and order.

Thus the month of June closed with the orphans in particular and residents in general happily looking forward to the Glorious Fourth, the City Council resting content in the knowledge that all municipal problems were under control, and the newspapers still confident and optimistic. For example, the *Bee* on June 30 editorialized: "Considering the unprecedented accumulation of filth—palpable to the eye and offensive to the nose—which exists at this time in our city, its sanitary condition is a subject of special congratulation." The editorial, which was headed "No More Yellow Fever," then asserted that although there had been little change for the better in the sanitary conditions, the health of the city had steadily improved. The editor noted that yellow fever had not been epidemic for six years and added that he did not believe it was "likely ever to reappear in that form." [31] Yet, despite the preoccupation with humdrum affairs and the customary gay atmosphere of the city which liked to describe itself as one which care had forgotten, one senses a vague uneasiness in the discussions of the City Council, a faint note of shrillness in the newspaper editorializing, and an occasional indication, in the references to the rumors spreading around the city, that all was not well. No one seriously believed that yellow fever was more than a casual threat—but one could never be sure.

This growing apprehension over the presence of yellow fever in New Orleans can be seen in the July 1 editorials of the two local medical journals. The conservative *New Orleans Medical & Surgical Journal*, under the editorship of Dr. Hester, played down the yellow fever situation. In an article on the city's health, the editor declared that measles and scarlatina had been the chief diseases during the past month, but that the townspeople had been unusually healthy. The city's hospitals had had relatively few cases of disease, "the best evidence," Hester wrote, "of the universal prevalence of public health among all classes of our population." Despite this cheerful comment, he urged the city officials to enforce all sanitary ordinances as strictly as possible. Almost as an afterthought, he mentioned that there had been twelve deaths from yellow fever in Charity Hospital up to the time of writing (June 22) and two or three more in private practice, but said he would reserve judgment on the subject until the next issue, "by which time it will be seen whether we have an epidemic or not." [32]

The *New Orleans Monthly Medical Register* could usually be counted on to take an aggressive stand on any and all issues, and its editor, Dr. Axson, did not pussyfoot on the yellow fever problem. He began his report on the city's health by pointing out that the deaths from yellow fever were already greater than those caused by any other fever. "This is an inauspicious opening for our summer and autumnal months," he wrote, and if the trend continues, "we are apt to have it in its most destructive intensity." [33] Like Fenner, he urged greater attention to sanitary problems and appealed for the creation of an effective nonpolitical board of health. Under the menacing threat of an approaching calamity, he declared, it was time men put aside their private interests and concentrated upon the public welfare.

On Saturday, July 2, the Physico-Medical Society, one of the two medical groups in New Orleans, met for its monthly meeting. Dr. E. D. Fenner, who also had no compunction about calling a spade a spade, read a paper on the current yellow fever outbreak in which he traced all known cases up to the time of writing. According to the minutes of the meeting, he accompanied his facts "with some well-timed and pertinent remarks on the sensitiveness manifested by our city authorities on the occurrence of any malignant or epidemical disorder." Anyone who dared "to hint the truth . . . often . . . was crushed with a load of ridicule and abuse, for his pains in announcing the coming danger." Dr. Axson appended an editorial note in his usual forceful—if involved—style, stating among other things that ever since 1848 "the Executive Administration of our city, in all matters pertaining to sanitary regulations, has been in charge of imbeciles, who seek to conceal their delinquencies . . . by a shameful suppression of the truth on all occasions of great public calamity from the visitation of pestilence." [34]

Whatever disagreements the local physicians may have had as to whether yellow fever would become epidemic, there could have been few, if any, who were unaware of its presence. Indeed, by this time there could have been few laymen who had not at least heard rumors of the disease. Even the newspaper editors, always the last to admit the possibility of an epidemic outbreak, began hedging a bit, turning from absolute denials to discounting the presence of what they termed a few sporadic cases. On July 2 the editorial columns of the *Bee* clearly demonstrated the ambivalence of its editors. Column one contained a short letter from "A Physician," attacking the paper for publishing an editorial entitled "No More Yellow Fever." The correspondent suggested that the editors walk through the wards of Charity Hospital if they had any doubts as to the presence of the disease. In outrage, the accused editors devoted the remainder of the column to denouncing the author and to proclaiming the virtues of a free press. Had the "Physician" read the original editorial more carefully, they stated, he would have realized that it had not denied the existence of a few sporadic cases but had said that "since the year 1847, Yellow Fever, as an EPIDEMIC had ceased to afflict us." In the process of attacking the "Physician" personally, the editorial declared: "He probably belongs to the class of crying philosophers—gloomy soothsayers—birds of ill-omen—medical Jeremiahs—who are ever presaging woe to our devoted city." Significantly, the editorial did not deny that both the number of cases and deaths were increasing.[35]

In the next column, under the heading "Our Climate," an editorial began: "Our city has rarely been more completely deserted than at present. Since the beginning of June a regular and uninterrupted stampede has been in progress. Every steamer has carried away a living freight, and the process of temporary depopulation has continued so rapidly, that now at the beginning of July, it is very questionable whether New Orleans contains one-half the number of those who reside amongst us during the Winter." After deriding those who fled from New Orleans to escape the heat and commenting upon the heat waves in the North, the editorial suggested that those wishing to leave the city would do far better by going to resorts on Lakes Pontchartrain and Borgne. Nowhere in the editorial was it even hinted that the presence of yellow fever may have had some bearing on the mass exodus.[36]

The next day, Sunday, the *Delta* also expatiated upon the felicitous climate of New Orleans: New Orleanians, the editor declared, should feel grateful "for the happy immunity we enjoy from anything like oppressive and unbearable heat," particularly in view of the intense heat waves experienced by the northern cities and the resultant "frightful mortality. . . . A cool, delicious breeze fans our cheeks at this moment," the editor rhapsodized, "and there is every indication of a most delightful summer's day." Like his colleague on the *Bee*, he sympathized with those residents who had mistakenly rushed north to avoid the heat.[37]

Recognizing by this time that the yellow fever could no longer be concealed, all the newspapers began publishing weekly reports from Charity Hospital, though their treatment of the facts varied considerably. On July 3 the *Picayune* simply gave the figures with an added notation that there had been 24 deaths from yellow fever in June and that 15 had occurred during the previous week.[38] On the same day the *Delta* published the weekly hospital report showing a total of 45 deaths from all causes, with 647 patients remaining in the institution. An almost too casual editorial note stated: "The greater number of those still inside are laboring under intermittent and remittent fevers. There are some cases of yellow fever, from which, if we mistake not, some few have died during the week." [39] The *Bee*, still determined to live up to its responsibility to protect the public from undue alarm, reported on Monday, July 4, that there had been 34 deaths (a figure which accorded with that of the *Picayune*) and that 655 patients remained in the hospital, but made no direct mention of yellow fever. In fact, the editorial positively exulted: "Only thirty-four deaths in the hospital in one week! Why, there were as many deaths in a single day, in New York, from sunstroke, the week before last." To bolster the editorial view, an adjacent column carried a news item reporting that 561 persons had died in New York the preceding week, due in part to the intense heat![40]

The Glorious Fourth temporarily halted all business activity in the city and, as might be expected, was celebrated in many different ways. The Sons of Temperance held their festivities at the Mechanics' Institute and, according to the advance program, enlivened the occasion "by vocal and instrumental music—Glees, Solos, Airs, Duets, &c., &c., by lady and gentlemen amateurs."

The weather was fine and the local military companies held their customary parades, after which they "embarked for the Lake shore, where they spent the day in the interchange of the most agreeable courtesies and hospitality." According to the newspapers, the children in the local orphanages had an especially good time. The girls from the Poydras Asylum joined the boys from the Fourth District Asylum and passed the day "in a happy manner." Their day was concluded with "a handsome repast" and the possibly dubious pleasure of listening "to an address delivered by [W.] C. Duncan, Esq." [41] Not all of the celebrations were in line with the martial displays of the militia, the clean Christian pleasures of the Sons of Temperance, or the wholesome joys of the orphans. On Tuesday following the holiday, the Recorders' Courts were filled with an unusual number of cases of drunk and disorderly conduct, though practically all of them were discharged "in consideration of the strong temptation which they had to celebrate the Glorious Fourth. They were generally admonished," the newspaper report said, "to keep sober until the next Anniversary of our National Independence." [42]

Having experienced some unaccustomed activity late in June, the City Council once more lapsed into lethargy. On Wednesday, July 5, both boards met officially, but the holiday evidently had taken its toll. Only four of the aldermen showed up and they promptly adjourned the meeting until the next Tuesday. The assistant aldermen turned out in adequate numbers but only discussed the failure of certain street contractors to fulfill their responsibilities. The main order of the day, the subject of establishing a board of health, was postponed until the next meeting.[43]

Aside from expressing their apprehension over the city's sanitary condition, the newspapers appeared to be preoccupied with the routine summer news. State and national politics, amusements, and items of local interest filled those columns devoted to city affairs. One of them began campaigning to get better salaries for the teachers—surprisingly, it favored equalizing the salaries of men and women teachers.[44] The Southern Museum, about the only theatre to remain open during the hot months, continued to provide the citizens with what was described as varied and attractive entertainment.[45] An unpleasant note was interjected when on July 10 one of the newspapers published a Charity Hospital report showing 62 deaths during the previous week with 725 patients under treatment. An explanatory note stated that half of the deaths were caused by yellow fever but that most of the patients were suffering from intermittent and bilious fevers. Two days later a grim news story gave emphasis to the spectre of yellow fever ominously hovering over the city; a delirious patient in Charity Hospital managed to escape and wandered around for several hours before he was located on the corner of St. John and Common streets. There he was found in a dying condition by the hospital attendants.[46]

The weather, which had turned unusually hot and dry throughout the entire state in June, changed drastically in early July. New Orleans was the first to get rain, on July 5, and the complaints about the dry spell soon gave way to those which deplored the dampness and excessive humidity. On July 12 the *Picayune* bemoaned: "Such weather is more than enough to give one both the 'sulks' and the 'blues.' Thoughts of suicide float before one; duns haunt one; the dinner is abominable; humanity is sour and crabbed; one could fight one's best friend at the least favorable opportunity. Damp, dingy, murky, misty, muzzy is the weather, and so we feel." [47] In other areas of Louisiana the drought continued, and newspaper reports indicated serious worries about crops. Beginning the same day that this editor was bewailing the weather, Baton Rouge, Iberville, Thibodaux, Madison, Morehouse, Opelousas, and Caddo reported cheerful news of rains which had come just in time to save the crops.[48] As the downpours continued, the rest of the state began to wonder whether a drought was being replaced by a flood.

In the week following the fourth of July, the number of yellow fever cases and deaths steadily crept upward, but a casual scanning of the newspapers indicates that there was little concern. In rereading the daily journals, the private correspondence, and the official records, one senses a feeling of anxiety—as if everyone were waiting with bated breath. The threat of an epidemic was looming larger and larger, but apparently no one wanted to admit it. Denouncing the filthy condition of the streets was a favorite pastime for New Orleans newspapermen, but this July there was a special urgency in their editorials. On the Wednesday after the Fourth, another daily journal voiced the fears of many old-time residents in an editorial which spoke of having seen for the past few weeks "every possible indication of a sickly season—fostered, if not directly produced, by the negligence, ignorance and laziness of the present city officials. The streets have looked and smelt [*sic*] epidemical for a fortnight," the editorial said, "and carrion and carcasses and festering nastiness of every description has been allowed to remain undisturbed and constantly augmented." [49]

CHAPTER III

Resolution of Doubt

For the first two weeks in July the city had marked time, scarcely daring to speculate on the extent of yellow fever. Whatever doubts may have been entertained regarding the seriousness of the outbreak were resolved with startling suddenness on July 13. On this date unobtrusive notices appeared in the newspapers announcing that a special meeting of the Howard Association would take place at seven o'clock the following day in the office of D. I. Ricardo, the group's secretary.[1] To old-time residents this brief notice spoke volumes. The Howard Association was a group of young businessmen who, during the periodic epidemics, dedicated themselves to caring for the sick. The association had first come into existence during the yellow fever outbreak of 1837, and the courage and devotion of its members had completely won the hearts of the citizens of New Orleans. Henceforth, in times of crisis, an appeal from the Howard Association was certain to bring an immediate and generous response. By its charter the organization was restricted to thirty members, but the events of the 1853 epidemic soon forced the group to double its numbers.

According to William L. Robinson, a member who later recorded his experiences during this epidemic, the association had actually gone to work before the announcement of the meeting on July 13. He wrote that early in July alarm "prevailed throughout the city" and everyone was preoccupied with rumors. The association had gone about its business quietly, for, he said, they "were requested by editors and merchants to withhold publication of our acts, as the report of an epidemic—which might yet be checked—would entail severe loss on merchants and shopkeepers." The decision to give public notice of their meeting, an act which would leave no doubt in the minds of residents that an epidemic was actually underway, was occasioned by the failure of the City Council's finance committee to make money available to the association. The council was still wrangling over the problem of cleaning the streets and had made no progress on the resolution to create a board of health. Regretfully concluding that no help was to be expected from this quarter, Robinson wrote, "we determined to act independently; to call upon the citizens for aid, and to assume the duties of a Board of Health." [2]

Only eighteen members attended the first meeting, the other twelve being absent from the city. Those present decided to issue a proclamation announcing that the fever had reached an epidemic stage and notifying the public that the association was preparing to meet the emergency. In the same announcement, they appealed to city authorities to appropriate funds to provide medicines for the sick poor. On the first day private citizens responded by donating over $15,000, and more physicians volunteered their services than the association could use. Swinging into action, the Howard Association first partitioned the city into districts, placed one member in each district, and gave him authority to investigate all cases of sickness, assign doctors, and authorize the purchase of drugs. In addition, the impoverished, who constituted the major share of the association's patients, were given food, bedding, and other essentials. The first step in organizing the work was to replace those members who were not available for service and thus bring the membership up to the maximum number of thirty. As the number of cases climbed into the thousands and more help was needed, the Howards evaded the constitutional restriction on total membership by choosing one assistant for each of the members. [3]

While the Howard Association was assuming responsibility, the council continued to debate what should be done. Even when the two boards were able to agree on a resolution appropriating money for some useful purpose, their inability to decide on the specific amount usually caused the resolution to fail. On July 12 both boards met and dealt with a few routine matters. For example, a petition to the Board of Assistant Aldermen stating that the captains of vessels in the port of the Second District "complain of the stench from the offal thrown into the river from opposite the meat market and Esplanade street" was referred to the committee on police. On recommendation of the committee on charity it was agreed to vote $50 to return a widow with four children to her home in Virginia after it was learned that her husband, in a fit of insanity, had jumped overboard during their trip to New Orleans. [4]

The Board of Aldermen, which met concurrently, spent considerable time discussing the city surveyor's estimate of the annual cost of cleaning the streets using city personnel instead of private contractors. The surveyor placed the cost of hiring carts and laborers at slightly over $90,000 but stated that he thought this sum could be reduced. Although the new system would be more expensive, he assured the board that the work would be performed more effectively. Both boards were so convinced of the need for drastic reform that they held a joint meeting that same night and selected a Mr. John Carbery as the new superintendent of carts and laborers, thus taking one more step toward eliminating the contractors.[5]

Two days later, the two city boards reassembled and once again took up the problem of the street contractors. The assistant aldermen's committee on streets and landings recommended immediate cancellation of all agreements with those individuals who had failed to live up to the terms of their street-cleaning contracts. Despite this seemingly strong action, when the street commissioner appealed for funds to hire twenty-five laborers to clean the Galvez Canal, which had become little more than a cesspool, neither the aldermen nor the assistant aldermen were willing to appropriate the money.[6] A letter from Mr. Ricardo of the Howard Association appealing for municipal funds to buy medicine was next brought to the attention of the boards. Assistant Alderman R. J. Ker resolved that the city subsidize medicine for the poor to the extent of $1,000. Mr. J. Gilmore amended the motion to read $2,000, and in this form it was passed by a vote of fourteen to two. By the time the resolution was sent to the aldermen for concurrence, however, the amount had been reduced to $1,000.[7]

For a few days following the Howard Association's meeting on July 14 the newspapers did not comment editorially on the event. They did, however, redouble their efforts to get action from the municipal authorities on the score of sanitation. The editor of one newspaper was particularly incensed over having seen one of the street cleaners leave a dead dog lying on one of the main streets. "He passed it as cooly and quietly as the warm weather would permit, and that bloated carcass will remain in that much frequented street for twenty-four hours longer." [8]

The *Delta* asked rhetorically if it was enough for the street contractors simply to rake the dirt into piles and leave it in the streets, as had happened on Gravier Street, where piles of filth had been lying for over a week. In view of the danger from yellow fever, the editor wrote, all possible sanitary precautions should be taken.[9] On July 14 the *Bee*, in a rather perceptive editorial, discussed the relation of filth to yellow fever. The editorial writer noted that in some of the preceding summers the city had been unusually dirty and yellow fever had not appeared. He did not question the widely accepted belief that most fevers were "the result of accumulated dirt, foul air, and impure water. . . . That filth is a prolific source of other disorders is a fact familiar to medical men. . . . Yet," he went on, "it is almost an established truth, that mere filth will not generate Yellow Fever. Something more is needed, but in what the essential condition consists, is, we believe, yet unknown." [10]

Although mention of yellow fever was beginning to creep into the newspapers, most of the editors appeared more concerned over the situation of the poor school teachers than of the threatening epidemic. One of them was shocked to discover a school district in which the directors had stopped the salaries of teachers on sick leave or on vacation.[11] In what was obviously becoming a time of crisis, the fact that the newspapers were devoting so much attention to school matters, including the annual school inspections, speaks well for the local school system. Despite the business-as-usual attitude of the city newspapers, small news items here and there gave evidence of the growing yellow fever crisis. On July 17 the following notice was carried in one of the editorial columns: "Whilst so many of our citizens are leaving, or have already left, our city, we take pleasure in stating that Dr. Charles E. Kells will remain and attend to the duties of his profession, at No. 106 Canal Street, second door from Bourbon." Dr. Kells, a dentist, was under no obligation to remain at his post, and his decision showed strong character.[12]

By Tuesday, July 19, when the City Council was scheduled to meet, the wards of Charity Hospital were filled with patients, and yellow fever cases were beginning to overflow into the halls. On this same day the Board of Aldermen held a long meeting and, according to one newspaper reporter, transacted a large amount of business "with the view of adjourning over for a recess until the 1st of October." [13] The board first considered letters from two physicians who offered their services for the care of the sick poor, but resolved to lay the communications on the table. Next, Alderman Converse offered a motion placing $5,000 at the disposal of the Howard Association, "to be used by them in alleviating the distress of the sick." After considerable discussion, the motion was amended to read $2,500 and in this form was unanimously agreed upon and sent to the Board of Assistant Aldermen for its concurrence. Somewhat more quickly the aldermen concurred in a resolution of the assistant aldermen authorizing the city to pay up

Whenever pestilence struck New Orleans, as it did in 1853, the great Charity Hospital was always ready to offer medical care to the destitute sick.

to $1,000 for medicines to be dispensed by the Howard Association. Mr. Converse moved that the city pay all apothecary bills incurred by the association during the coming four months, since he felt that $1,000 might be inadequate. His motion, however, was defeated. The board also rejected a proposal by the assistant aldermen to utilize the fines collected during the summer months for "the relief of the sick and destitute." Having voted a pittance to provide for the sick—the number of deaths had already exceeded 300—the aldermen, no doubt suffused with virtue at their generosity, resolved that the next meeting should be held on the third Tuesday of the following October. Before adjourning, they held a brief joint session with the assistant aldermen to elect certain municipal officials.[14]

The assistant aldermen were in no more generous mood. Upon considering the aldermen's proposal to place $2,500 at the disposal of the Howard Association for the distress of the sick poor, Mr. T. O. Stark promptly moved that the amount be reduced to $2,000. After debate, both the motion and the amendment were laid on the table. Following further parliamentary maneuvering, the motion was reconsidered and passed by a vote of 13 to 4. As the required majority was 14 out of the 27 members, the motion was lost for want of a legal majority.[15]

The Board of Assistant Aldermen now turned to more serious business. A long preamble and a series of resolutions were offered by Mr. P. C. Wright proposing that the judicial committee prepare articles of impeachment against the street commissioner, James Jolls. Jolls was accused, among other things, of "a gross and unpardonable neglect of his duty, notwithstanding repeated admonitions from the council and ample provisions made for the efficient performance of the services and functions for which the office filled by him was created. . . ." Mr. Jolls, like other citizens familiar with the workings of the city government, must scarcely have known whether to laugh or cry at the phrase "ample provisions made for the efficient performance. . . ." He was further accused of "setting at defiance the authority of the common council and using with regard to the members thereof individually and collectively the most opprobrious and disgusting epithets." Jolls had repeatedly appeared before the City Council appealing for strong action against negligent contractors and for funds to hire the needed labor to remedy the worst sanitary conditions, and it is not at all unlikely that he gave vent to his frustrations on occasion. In any case, after discussing and slightly moderating the tone of the resolutions, the assistant aldermen voted 18 to 3 in favor of them.[16]

By this time it was apparent to everyone that New Orleans was facing a full-scale epidemic, and there can be little doubt that the city councilmen were desperately hunting a scapegoat. Prodded by their own sense of guilt—they could scarcely have been unaware of their failure to create a board of health and of the niggardly sums appropriated for cleaning the city—the councilmen were determined to appear in the public eye as men of action, leaders prepared to place the blame squarely upon the shoulders of those responsible. The fact that the office of street commissioner was a notorious political football and that the council members themselves looked upon the street-cleaning contracts as a form of patronage only served to increase their indignation.

The City Council's hope, conscious or otherwise, that the charges against Jolls would direct public attention away from its own negligence proved illusory. With rare unanimity New Orleans papers criticized the council's action. The *Bee* ridiculed the accusation that Jolls had called the assistant aldermen "very naughty names," and condemned equally the idea that the street commissioner should be held responsible for the epidemic. The people, it stated, "are not so green as the Locofoco Aldermen imagine. They and they alone, will be held responsible for any shortcomings." [17]

The *Delta* laid the blame equally on both parties. The impeachment charges had come too late, it asserted, since the city "is beleaguered night and day, and it is useless to try to conceal the fact any longer." Jolls, the newspaper said, was "notoriously incapable or idle," but the real problem lay with the council. Over two months before, the council had declared the office of street commissioner to be useless, yet it had done absolutely nothing about the streets and had voted only a meager appropriation for the Howard Association. For weeks the municipal authorities had been attempting to conceal the ravages of yellow fever, but, the *Delta* proclaimed virtuously: "An epidemic cannot be concealed. You might as well strive to hide the sun or moon." [18]

The *Crescent*, too, condemned both Jolls and the City Council, although, like the *Delta*, it was inclined to place the major blame upon the council. In a sarcastic editorial the paper accused the council of denouncing the street commissioner in order to cover up its own negligence. The *Picayune*, on the other hand, took heart at the council's action, declaring it a sign of vigor indicating that the council was at last awakening to its responsibilities. "If there is not an epidemic upon us," one of its editorials asserted, "there is in certain portions of the city an amount of disease of a malignant and fatal character, which gives just cause for anxiety, and requires prompt and thorough and unstinted measures." Only the *Commercial Bulletin* spoke up for the street commissioner. The real difficulty, its editor stated, arose from several factors, including inadequate grading of the streets, insufficient funds for sanitary purposes, and the fact that the whole system needed a complete overhauling.[19]

On July 22 one journalist summed up the attitude of the local newspapers when he declared that all of them were agreed that it was idle to place the responsibility solely upon the street commissioner. He suggested that as a temporary expedient citizens in the various wards form their own health committees. The writer pointed out that the street commissioner had only advisory powers and that the contractors could defy his authority and laugh at his threats. Only by giving him real power and eliminating the contract system would the problem be solved.[20]

The attack on James Jolls in the City Council meeting of Tuesday, July 19, brought the whole yellow fever question out into the open, and it soon became a general topic for discussion in the newspapers. The *Crescent*, on this same day, in publishing the Board of Health's weekly list of burials noted that yellow fever was on the increase and that the number of deaths had quadrupled in the past three weeks.[21] The *Delta*, which on July 21 was to accuse the city officials of trying to conceal the epidemic, as late as July 20 was still cheerfully denying the presence of epidemic yellow fever. While deploring the many exaggerated rumors with respect to the city's health, it did concede that yellow fever was present, "but not, we think, to such an extent as to create any serious alarm, either at home or abroad." As a matter of fact, the paper went on, yellow fever was much easier to treat than other fevers: all one needed to do was take proper care, live a temperate life, and keep one's stomach healthy. For those who used discretion, it said confidently, an attack of yellow fever was usually beneficial: "It reconstitutes and re-organizes the system, and makes a man almost proof thereafter against disease. Unlike typhoid, and other fevers, its after effects are not only innocent, but in fact invigorating." [22]

Le Courrier, while not as sanguine, also sought to reassure its readers. Its policy, the editor wrote, was neither to spread needless alarms nor to conceal the presence of the disease. During the past week, 204 of the 304 deaths in the city had resulted from yellow fever, and the number of yellow fever cases was still increasing. In the Fourth District—formerly known as Lafayette—the disease, according to "respectable physicians,"

Le Courrier went on, only imprudent strangers were falling victim to the outbreak; those strangers who used discretion and met the yellow fever with calmness had nothing to fear. Moreover, the fever was not as malignant as it had been previously, and the medical faculty had now learned to deal with it.[23]

There was need for reassurance at this time. Up to July 2, a total of 47 individuals had died of yellow fever. From July 2 to July 9 the death toll jumped to 59; the following week 204 deaths were recorded; and in the week from July 16 to July 23 no less than 429 persons succumbed to yellow fever. By the last week in July, the death toll was averaging better than 80 per day. It was under these conditions that the newspapers were conceding that the disease might be epidemic![24]

When the Common Council met on Friday, July 22, the deaths from yellow fever for the preceding week exceeded 400, and it was obvious to everyone that New Orleans was facing a real crisis. The Board of Aldermen, which had already voted to adjourn for the summer, was summoned back into session on this day by Mayor Crossman. Only seven of the twelve members showed up as the meeting got underway, a bare quorum. After passing a series of resolutions relating to sanitation and sending them on to the Board of Assistant Aldermen for concurrence, the aldermen got down to the main business, the establishment of a board of health. A long resolution consisting of nine articles was proposed by a Mr. Burke. After a relatively brief discussion and some amendment, the proposal to establish a health board was sent to the assistant aldermen for concurrence. In brief the ordinance proposed to create a board of health consisting of fifteen persons appointed by the mayor, not more than half of whom were to be practicing physicians. Two health wardens were to be appointed in each of the city's eleven districts at a salary not to exceed $30 per month. The board was also to appoint a health physician whose duty it would be to enter every vessel coming into the port of New Orleans and investigate whether the ship carried any epidemic diseases. For these services, the physician was to collect $10 from each ship captain. [25]

The Board of Assistant Aldermen met almost at the same time, and their meeting was opened by Mr. P. C. Wright, who offered a preamble and a series of resolutions. In his introduction, he drew the board's attention to the existence of a disease of "unparalleled fatality" which might well become epidemic as a result of the filthy condition of the city, and he warned the Common Council of New Orleans that it would be held accountable unless it lived up to its responsibilities. When the

Board of Aldermen adjourned until late in October, they left the "Assistant Board powerless to act effectively." Consequently, he urged that every member of the Common Council remain at his post until the danger was over; that a board of health be established; that the mayor recall the Board of Aldermen; and that a temporary health board enforce all sanitary measures until the permanent board could take over. The resolutions were adopted by a vote of 12 to 1. A motion was then made to appropriate an additional $2,000 for the Howard Association. In the discussion which followed, the amount was raised to $2,500 and the wording amended so as to place the money at the disposal of the temporary health committee.[26]

In health matters the council, like city policy-making bodies in general, was always happy to pass resolutions so long as they did not involve spending money. Thus when a resolution was received from the Board of Aldermen suggesting the appointment of a special joint committee of four members from each board to purchase up to one thousand barrels of lime for disinfecting the streets, the assistant aldermen promptly rejected the proposal. The same treatment was given another measure authorizing the street commissioner to hire up to two hundred men and as many horses and carts as necessary to be "employed in cleaning the streets and liming the gutters" for a period of fifteen days. In justice, it should be pointed out that Dr. S. W. Dalton, the president of the board, was firmly convinced that lime was of no value as a disinfecting agent and so opposed all appropriations for this purpose.[27]

Despite their reluctance to dispense tax funds, the assistant aldermen did agree to spend thirty dollars to hire two men for a month to remove the dead dogs, cows, and other carcasses floating along the wharves. They further agreed to procure eight wagons equipped with mattresses "for the conveyance of the poor sick to the Hospital." Having stretched their benevolence to the limit, they quickly and decisively voted 11 to 2 against a proposal to permit the street commissioner to hire fifteen deputies to serve as sanitary inspectors. The council, however, was not likely to strengthen the hand of the street commissioner, since during this same meeting they voted to sustain three of the charges of impeachment against him. Assistant Alderman O'Sullivan moved to suspend Street Commissioner Jolls and to use his salary to employ district commissioners. Fortunately for the cause of justice, the presiding officer ruled O'Sullivan's motion out of order on the grounds that Jolls had not actually been impeached. Before adjourning, the board voted to request a joint meeting with the aldermen to establish a board of health, but no further steps were taken.[28]

For the week ending Saturday, July 23, the official figures from the cemeteries showed that 617 burials had taken place; 429 of these deaths were attributed to yellow fever. The City Council, under pressure from the newspapers and other public agencies, had done little but debate. A few meager sums had been appropriated for sanitary purposes; impeachment charges had been brought against the street commissioner, presumably to encourage him to be more conscientious; several city officials had been given leaves of absence for the summer, including the city treasurer; and there was still no city board of health. The Board of Assistant Aldermen was willing to continue its biweekly meetings, but the aldermen had adjourned until late in October—the end of the yellow fever season.

The newspapers that weekend were not nearly as bitter as one might have expected. The *Picayune* did contrast the philanthropy of those physicians who had volunteered their services with the attitude of the municipal councilors who had refused even to provide financial support for the Howard Association. The actions of the City Council in its Friday meeting, the paper declared, could be summed up in one line: "They met, disagreed, did nothing and adjourned." After pointing out in a conciliatory fashion that individually the boards had passed some sound measures, only to have them fail because of the inability of the two boards to concur, the editor appealed to the councilmen to take the leadership and assume responsibility for the city's health.[29]

The *Delta*, having taken the plunge and conceded the presence of yellow fever a couple of days earlier, announced on Sunday, July 24: "It is with deep sorrow and regret that we feel bound to admit that the Yellow Fever prevails in this city to an extent equal, if not surpassing, almost any previous year of its history." The newspapers, it continued, were not to blame for the delay in pronouncing the disease epidemic, since it had been the usual custom to wait for the Board of Health to take the initiative, but this time there was no board of health! Lest its readers get too discouraged by the news of so many yellow fever deaths in the weekly Charity Hospital report, the *Delta* editorially noted that Dr. Dalton, a physician and president of the Board of Assistant Aldermen, had studied the cases of yellow fever closely and was "firmly convinced that the disease at present in our city is not by any means epidemic." Dr. Dalton believed that the disease was merely sporadic and in any case was restricted to immigrants and other new arrivals. It is difficult to say whether Dalton's views explain his opposition to any action on the part of the City Council or whether his opposition to spending the taxpayers' money explains his medical views.[30]

Mayor Crossman, determined to get action out of the council, called both boards into session again on Monday, July 25. The aldermen met and, after agreeing to send a messenger to the assistant aldermen asking their concurrence in an ordinance creating a board of health, voted to table a resolution from their colleagues on the other board to hold a joint meeting. With unusual speed and generosity, they then voted to appropriate $10,000 to be placed at the discretion of the proposed health board. After a recess, word was received that the assistant aldermen had accepted—with minor amendments—the proposed board of health.[31]

The meeting of the Board of Assistant Aldermen on this day was a little more stormy. After hearing a message from the mayor explaining that he had called the two boards into session because of the desperate need for a health board, Mr. Stark opened the discussion by offering the measure to create a 15-man board of health which had been drawn up earlier by the joint committee of the Common Council. Assistant Alderman Wright immediately moved to substitute another measure, designed by Dr. Dalton, which would have designated the presidents of the two Common Council boards as the chief health officers. This latter resolution was tabled, and the assistant aldermen returned to Mr. Stark's original proposal. Most of the debate centered around the provision limiting the number of physicians on the health board to not more than half of the total membership. Mr. Vanderlinden suggested that the number of physicians be limited to four, but his motion was tabled. Dr. Dalton objected to any limitation on the number of physicians and became quite irritated in the course of the debate. What actually happened is best described in the words of a reporter for the *Bee* who stated that when Dr. Dalton was "told that doctors theorized too much," he replied that the board would probably consist of "seven thinking men and eight fools." [32] Despite his objections, the ordinance was adopted. Immediately the assistant aldermen took up the resolution from the Board of Aldermen to appropriate $10,000 for the newly created Board of Health and gave it their approval. At eight o'clock this same day, the two boards met in joint session and proceeded to select the members of the Board of Health. No doubt to Dr. Dalton's dismay, only five physicians were among the fifteen men chosen.[33]

The assistant aldermen, having voted to stay at their posts, held two more sessions. At their meeting on Tuesday, July 26, virtually no business was transacted save the passage of a resolution by a vote of 10 to 8 calling for adjournment until the second Tuesday in October.[34] Mayor Crossman, beset by a multitude of problems and desperately in need of assistance, again called the assistant aldermen to a special session on Thursday. Only eight members were present when the roll was called, and for lack of a quorum the meeting adjourned.[35] Thereafter the mayor was left to struggle along as best he could with the assistance of the Board of Health and the volunteer organizations. Of the twenty-seven assistant aldermen and twelve aldermen, about one third remained in the city and worked individually or through one of the voluntary associations to help the city survive its greatest tragedy; the rest followed the policy of many of the so-called "better class" and fled to safer locations.

Precisely at the time when the epidemic had become general and the numbers of sick and dying had reached such proportions that ordinary facilities could no longer provide for them, the City Council chose to adjourn for the summer. This reprehensible act of cowardice can scarcely be justified, though these individuals should not be judged in the light of present concepts of municipal responsibility. Epidemics were still viewed in part as acts of God, and health was considered primarily an individual responsibility. Although men of vision had been asserting for many years that maintaining public health was necessarily a collective responsibility, this idea had not yet gained much recognition. Moreover, the prevailing doctrine of laissez-faire—which maintained in effect that the least government was the best government—gave further support to the assumption by most of the councilmen that helping the sick poor was a responsibility of private charity. In precipitately adjourning and fleeing the city, the New Orleans councilmen were doing no more and no less than their counterparts in other cities of the United States had done and were doing during outbreaks of the great killer diseases. Rather than condemn those who fled, one must give credit to Mayor Crossman and those members of the city administration who risked their health and lives to do what they felt was their duty. In the nightmare which followed, these men may well have wondered about the wisdom of their decisions to remain.

CHAPTER IV

Days of Crisis

WHILE THE CITY COUNCIL was debating and the Howard Association was acting, deaths from yellow fever mounted alarmingly. For several weeks thousands of frantic people had been pouring out of the stricken city. The scene is best described in George Washington Cable's words: "Everywhere porters were tossing trunks into wagons, carriages rattling over the stones and whirling out across the broad white levee to the steamboats' sides. Foot-passengers were hurrying along the sidewalk, luggage and children in hand, and out of breath, many a one with the plague already in his pulse. The fleeing crowd was numbered by thousands." [1] By the end of July all who could leave were gone, and those who remained settled down resolutely to the task of caring for the sick and dying. As the hospitals filled to overflowing and bodies began to pile up at the cemeteries, the work awaiting the able-bodied seemed almost insurmountable. Doctors and druggists found themselves on constant call; men and women with no nursing experience were pressed into service; clerks and businessmen became relief administrators and welfare workers; and every available person was called upon to carry food to the sick, the serious cases to the hospitals, and the dead to the cemeteries.

In the middle of July, when it had become apparent that a serious epidemic was in the making but while the number of sick was still within manageable bounds, several national and/or cultural groups joined the Howard Association in caring for the sick. These agencies—such as the German Society of New Orleans and the Portuguese Benevolent Society—were designed to assist newly arrived immigrants, but in times of crisis they also served as benevolent and charitable bodies. It was well that they were in operation since immigrant vessels continued to arrive throughout July and August. Mayor Crossman, in calling the Common Council into extraordinary sessions, had specifically mentioned the danger to newcomers; one of the first acts of the Board of Health was to place a quarantine on incoming vessels to prevent the passengers and crews from adding fresh fuel to the epidemic flames.

As the number of burials increased, occasional incidents arose which disturbed the more conscientious citizens. On July 21 *Le Courrier* reported the case of an impoverished German woman who had died of yellow fever. The city had sent a cart of the type commonly used for hauling dirt or dung loaded with two coffins; the body was crammed into one of the coffins which proved too small, whereupon the men in charge jammed the lid shut "at the cost of cruelly mangling her face and crushing her head." Its reporter expressed both horror and indignation at the treatment accorded the woman's body and hoped that such incidents would not be repeated.[2] Increasingly, as the days went by, reports were published of yellow fever deaths occurring in public places. For example, on July 25 an inquest was held over the body of an unknown German who had asked for a drink of water at a house and fallen dead with yellow fever.[3]

Meanwhile the mass exodus from New Orleans had the effect of broadcasting the news of the yellow fever outbreak and of spreading the disease itself. The more New Orleans papers played down the seriousness of the epidemic, the more newspapers outside the city, in a rather curious inverse ratio, exaggerated its effects. On July 23 a Mississippi newspaper reported that yellow fever was daily destroying 200 persons in New Orleans. The *Picayune*, which picked up the quotation a couple of days later, remonstrated only mildly with the editor for letting his imagination run away with him.[4] By this date, too, the towns up the river from New Orleans were beginning to institute quarantines against the plague-stricken city. A health committee organized in Natchez set up a quarantine station below the town requiring that all persons from New Orleans be detained for seventy-two hours. Their baggage, along with all other goods coming from yellow fever areas, was to be opened and aired for a minimum of eight to ten hours.[5]

In New Orleans the heavy rains which had broken the hot, dry spell in June continued to fall, and from other sections of the state came reports of downpours and resultant damage to crops. The cotton growers, whose crops had benefited from the first rains, soon began to worry about the continuous showers, since wet weather in the latter stages could prove disastrous to the opening bolls. In New Orleans the damp, humid weather posed no direct economic threat, but it was depressing under the best of conditions, and the city had more than enough problems as July advanced. Moreover, in the desperate effort to explain the recurrent pestilential epidemics, medical thought had concentrated upon meteorological phenomena as part of what was called the "epidemic constitution," and the gloomy weather must have done much to aggravate fears in the troubled city. Around the end of July what may have been a cold front hit the city, leading one newspaper to comment: "Will any one tell us what time of the year it is? It certainly is not July. Last night it was cold enough for blankets. A sharp north wind blew all night. Bad time for patients! So much greater the need for care and attention." [6]

As business and social activity almost ceased, the newspapers, unwilling to publish information about the fever, were hard put for local news. On July 28 the *Bee*, under the caption "City Intelligence," had remarked: "A DULL DAY.—Yesterday was emphatically a dull day in the way of police items and other intelligence. There was not a respectable case before any of the Recorders, and in the District Courts we could not discover the wherewithal to make up a decent paragraph. Only a few promissory note suits rewarded the diligence of the Reporters, and it is not considered *comme il faut* to report them." [7] If the police report was dull, there was good reason for it. With the city half empty and economic activity virtually halted, thieves, pickpockets, and other criminals would find pickings slim indeed in New Orleans.

If life appeared dull during the latter part of July, it was no fault of men like Dr. J. S. McFarlane and Dr. S. W. Dalton. Dr. Dalton was happily fighting the drive to create a board of health and waging particular war against spending city funds for sprinkling lime in the streets and gutters. In a letter explaining his views to the editor of a leading newspaper he said, on July 26, that he had been induced to write since he understood that he had "been censored by some, for my opposition to the foolish and worse than useless expenditure of thousands for distributing common lime about our streets to drive off the yellow fever." He had taken this position, he concluded, out of a sense of duty to himself and to the people of New Orleans. [8]

While Dr. Dalton's position was simply overruled by the other members of the City Council, Dr. McFarlane literally outraged the vast majority of respectable citizens by emphatically opposing not only the creation of a health board but all sanitary measures associated with it. He had earlier engaged in a vituperative exchange with Dr. Edward H.

Barton and the other leading sanitary reformers in New Orleans, and because of his intemperance he lost hearers even on those occasions when he was right. In brief, his thesis was that dirt and filth, far from contributing to outbreaks of yellow fever, actually had the opposite effect! In an age when the sanitary reformers were just beginning to gain widespread support and when, from an empirical standpoint, sanitation and cleanliness had demonstrably lowered sickness rates, McFarlane was bound to bring down upon his head the wrath of every reformer and respectable citizen. Ironically, in this instance, McFarlane was correct in his assertion that the causative agent of yellow fever was not to be found in dirt and filth. Yet draining the streets and open pools on public and private property probably did help to reduce the number of mosquitoes, though whether it would be enough to affect the spread of yellow fever is hard to say.[9]

McFarlane might have had more success had he been a little more reasonable in his approach, for other men were also puzzled by the inconsistencies between the spread of yellow fever and other contagious diseases. Typical of the way in which Dr. McFarlane's abusive tone nullified a sound argument is the following: "What can be expected from the wild vagaries of monomaniacs, who, wrapped in halcyon delusions, . . . refuse to contemplate the fact that cities, whose hygienic police almost approach perfection, possessing subterranean drainage, with a soil immeasurably less calculated to produce disease than ours, and possessing a fixed resident refined population, have for ages been periodically devastated by epidemic yellow fevers?"[10] Under the circumstances, neither the "monomaniacs" to whom the appeal was addressed nor the public which looked with considerable contempt upon the quarrels within the medical profession were likely to recognize the fundamental merit of McFarlane's argument. After the newspapers had derided his assertion that the dirt and filth tended to retard the formation of yellow fever, the good doctor appealed for a calm and reasonable discussion of his views. "There is one favor, however, I have to ask of you, gentlemen," he addressed the editors, "and that is, that should my opinion be honored by the notice of any other gentleman, you will permit no ascerbity, scurrility or personality to find a place in your columns. I wish to conduct this discussion, should a discussion arise, as a philosopher, and the weather is too warm to make it agreeable to get heated by controversy."[11]

In the long and involved letters and editorials which followed, Dr. McFarlane used what for him was unusual restraint; but as his arguments continued to fall upon deaf ears and his advice was scorned, his blood pressure and temperature gradually rose. In denouncing the editor of the *Crescent* in particular and his other adversaries in general, McFarlane angrily asserted: "Could any but a blind idiot, or one besotted by ancient prejudices, fail to perceive that *from the first moment the Board of Health went into operation, and commenced its lustrations, that the mortality in our city has increased in a duplicate ratio?*" The "so-called Board of Health," he went on, "can do no earthly good, but to stir up mud in the streets, and furnish a daily record of the dead, which, from the tone of the public prints, nobody believes." To pay for these "great accomplishments," the taxpayers would be assessed some twenty or thirty thousand dollars, "besides our other sources of inordinate taxation." Like Dr. Dalton, McFarlane had a keen appreciation for money and saw little point in wasting it on impoverished and dissolute strangers.[12]

While this debate raged, the newly created Board of Health swung into action. With Mayor Crossman as the presiding officer, a meeting was held at noon on Tuesday, July 26. Dr. A. F. Axson was elected permanent secretary and Dr. Abner Hester was chosen as port physician.[13] The selection of these two men was wise; both were forthright, intelligent citizens, and by virtue of their respective editorships of the New Orleans medical journals, they exercised considerable influence over the medical profession. Neither of them, moreover, was likely to give way to pressure from either business or political interests. In two successive meetings on Tuesday and Wednesday health wardens were selected, a decision was made to collect and publish the daily burial records from all cemeteries, and the duties of the various health officers were outlined.[14] By Friday, July 29, the Board of Health had organized a staff for the purpose of enforcing all sanitary regulations, and henceforth the board was to meet almost daily until the epidemic subsided.

It should be understood that the care of the poor and sick was not considered within the proper sphere of the Board of Health. Its primary purpose was to prevent the spread of disease, and its members, like the public in general, thought that this could best be achieved by eliminating all foul odors or miasmas. For example, the board at its Friday meeting resolved: "That it shall be the duty of the Health Wardens, strictly to inspect the streets, alleys, yards, privies, open lots and squares, of their respective Wards; to report the condition, if exceptionable, to the owners, residents and Board of Health; and if they find any nuisances affecting, or which they believe will affect the public health, they will leave with the person having authority over the same, the tenant of the premises, a written notice to remove the same within 24 hours." [15] Other board resolutions directed the wardens to submit full written reports of the conditions within their districts at least once a week and ordered that the names and addresses of all health wardens be published in the newspapers and that "Health Warden" signs be posted at their residences.[16]

Since the original sections of New Orleans had been built upon a natural levee, which had been further heightened as the years passed, the natural drainage of all streets was away from the river in the direction of the swamp leading ultimately to Lake Pontchartrain. Whatever may have been the disadvantages of this drainage system, it was possible to flush the gutters by means of hydrants located at the heads of those streets running diagonally from the river. In its aim to keep the streets as clean as possible, the Board of Health ordered that public hydrants on the main streets be opened for one hour each morning and evening.[17] The 60-inch annual rainfall in New Orleans originally had been sufficient to clean out the gutters, but as the population grew and the dirt and refuse accumulated, the rain water soon proved inadequate. Cities in the nineteenth century recruited their populations largely from rural areas, and these newcomers were accustomed to tossing their garbage, "night soil," and refuse into the yard or street. Moreover, hotels and large institutions frequently allowed their cesspools and privies to overflow into the gutters, and dead animals often added further distinction to the summer atmosphere. Whatever impact flushing the gutters may have had on health—and this is a debatable point—the aesthetic results must have justified the practice. Its first week's work completed, the board ordered that all of its actions and resolutions be published in the newspapers and that three thousand handbills bearing this information be printed for general distribution. Of these, two thousand were to be printed in English, five hundred in French, and another five hundred in German.[18]

Newspaper reaction to the establishment of a board of health was quite favorable, though comments were tempered by some reservations. One editor was too bitter over the council's delay to express much enthusiasm over the final creation of the health board. His account of the proceedings of the July 26 meeting of the Board of Assistant Aldermen was printed under the descriptive title, "Want of Dignity and Moral Cowardice." When the move for adjournment was made, he wrote, one reporter was heard to mutter, "I move you adjourn now and forever more." After summarizing the meeting, the editor concluded with the hope that for the credit of the city such a farce might never be repeated. The quarantine measures, which irritated many residents, drew praise from this same writer, who urged that they be strictly enforced. He also expressed the hope that a rigid application of the sanitary regulations would keep the pestilence within reasonable bounds until the frosts of fall ended its deadly work.[19]

The *Picayune* took the attitude that the creation of a board of health was a step in the right direction; its editor hoped that all those selected for "this extremely responsible trust" would accept the appointment and thus entitle themselves to the lasting gratitude of the city.[20] The *Bee* was far less optimistic than the other daily journals. It excoriated the council for its delay and warned its readers that it was too late to expect any immediate and direct benefits from the Board of Health. The council, it said, had "procrastinated beyond the limit of safety"; it had waited until yellow fever was killing its victims at the rate of sixty to seventy a day, "and then, when too late for any important practical good, yielded to the public clamor it had so long resisted and created the Board." Unfortunately, it continued, there was little that the board could do. While it was agreed that dirt and filth intensified yellow fever, the disease was not generated by this source. All experience had shown that once the disorder broke out in epidemic form, it was certain to run its course. Medicine could do nothing more than mitigate the fever's effects upon those who sought immediate help at its onset. It was to be hoped that cleansing the city would reduce the intensity of the outbreak in the crowded and dirty slum areas, but there was no guarantee even of this. In fact, all that the health board could do was "to counsel the unacclimated to use every means of safety, root out accumulations of offal and impurity, and maintain a daily and accurate record of the mortality." [21]

Soul-searching about their responsibility to the readers and to the advertisers had characterized the editorial columns of the New Orleans newspapers in the early weeks of the outbreak, and this attitude continued throughout July. On July 25, under the heading, "What is Our Duty?" a newspaperman reported that conversations with "several respectable physicians" had shown the disease to be serious but confined mainly to certain localities in the poorer sections of town. The large number of cases to be found in Charity Hospital was not too significant since nearly all of the sick poor were sent there. However, the fact that the poor were the chief sufferers was no excuse for neglect or inaction since all classes had a moral obligation to help them.[22]

Two days later this journal again discussed the state of the city's health in another long editorial: "The truth is, the disease existed in our midst long before it was acknowledged and proclaimed." During the previous week some 617 deaths had been reported, indicating an unprecedented malignity. The disease should have been announced earlier and sanitary preparations made for it. The one consolation, the paper continued, was that the epidemic was confined almost solely to the poor immigrant class and hence had occasioned no unnecessary alarm.[23] By way of reassurance, a note attached to the Charity Hospital report showing that eighty new cases had been admitted the previous day stated that several of these patients had been released in sound health. Nervous apprehensions, it seems, had caused individuals with minor complaints to assume that they had yellow fever.[24]

If this editor found no unnecessary alarm, he obviously was not moving in the same circles as his colleagues on the Bee. On July 29, in in an editorial entitled "The Fever," the latter stated: "We have never seen such a veritable stampede as the epidemic has occasioned. Thousands who had lived among us for six, or eight, or ten years—who had passed unscathed through the Fever of 1847—and who were wont to consider themselves proof against its attacks, have taken the alarm, and scampered away with the most commendable attention to their own safety. We do not think New Orleans has ever been as completely deserted by her merchants and professional men as she is now." The editor estimated that no less than twenty thousand people had fled to the safety of the shores of Lake Pontchartrain and thousands more were to be found on the Gulf Coast. In fact, he said, the chief hope for the city lay in the fact that seven-eighths of all the unacclimated had already fled.[25]

By July 30, with the daily death toll close to one hundred, the Picayune found little to be hopeful about, though it understood that the physicians had found the disease becoming slightly more manageable and that more patients were recovering. However, cases were appearing in all sections of the city, and many areas previously free of the disorder were starting to feel its effects. Contrary to the Bee, which felt that the number of unacclimated was relatively small (referring probably to the upper classes), the Picayune asserted: "During no previous epidemic were there ever so many strangers of the poorer unacclimated classes in New Orleans"; furthermore, the indications were "not encouraging at present for a mitigation of the epidemic, except from a diminution of subjects or a great & favorable change of weather." Nothing could avail save "patience, public & private exertion to remove or counteract all influences supposed to foster disease; [and] Christian kindness & charity to the sick." [26]

Even at this late date there were still unreconciled members of the medical profession who refused to concede that the disease was epidemic. On July 30 the *Delta* reported that "a prominent member of the faculty" had complained about the paper's editorial policy of speaking openly of the epidemic. This action, he was supposed to have said, was incorrect, impolitic, and harmful, and served only to create panic and unnecessary fears. The paper argued that in actuality it should have proclaimed the outbreak sooner, but explained that it had deferred to the authority of higher officials who were waiting "until our Doctors came to some agreement as to what is an epidemic and what [is] a sporadic form of the disease." [27]

In the nineteenth century, whenever pestilence struck at New Orleans, two agencies were always ready to offer medical care to the destitute sick. The great Charity Hospital of New Orleans had been in operation for over a hundred years before the epidemic of 1853. In all this time the sick or dying were accepted without question, and the ablest professors at the medical school served them. Neither race, nationality, age, nor sex barred any one from admission; although state and municipal funds were the chief source of income for the hospital, surprisingly few of the patients were Louisianians. In the late 1840's and early 1850's, as the tide of Irish and German migration mounted, the wards of Charity were filled with sick immigrants. Victimized by ruthless ship captains and owners who herded these immigrants into the holds of their ships in unbelievable numbers, the newcomers often landed in New Orleans and other American port cities in a deplorable state. Typhus was rife on the vessels, and respiratory and enteric diseases flourished in the dirty, poorly ventilated, and crowded cabins and holds. The death rate on the passage over became an international scandal, and it was small wonder that many who survived the voyage were too sick to work.

The hospital was administered by the Sisters of Charity, a Catholic nursing order which had been established at Emmitsburg, Maryland, earlier in the century. In the twenty years they had served in New Orleans, these kindly Sisters had survived crisis after crisis, had seen epidemics of Asiatic cholera, yellow fever, smallpox and typhus, and were well prepared to meet the new threat from yellow fever. On earlier occasions, as the wards and halls had filled up with patients, the Sisters had surrendered a good part of their living accommodations to make room for additional sick.[28] Long before there was any official acknowl-

One of the Sisters of Charity who administered Charity Hospital. During epidemics, the Sisters frequently gave up a good part of their living quarters to make room for additional patients.

edgment of the existence of yellow fever in 1853, the staff of Charity was already at work, and the growing number of admissions gave early indication of the accelerating tempo of the epidemic. By the middle of July the hospital was filled to capacity; within a few days there was scarcely room for the staff to work.

The second organization, the Howard Association, undoubtedly rendered more help to the citizens of New Orleans in times of major medical crises than any other single body. By the middle of July, as mentioned earlier, its membership was fully organized and its work well underway. The names and addresses of members and assistants were published in all the newspapers along with a brief notice stating that anyone needing help could apply to the member living closest to him. Since the Howards relied largely upon private donations, the names of those individuals designated as collectors for the association were published, along with the names and addresses of physicians and apothecaries cooperating with the Howards. The association's apothecaries were provided with slates upon which those needing help could write their names. The Howard members for each district checked the slates twice a day and investigated all cases. If the patient could be moved, he was taken to a hospital; otherwise the association provided a doctor and a nurse. It was the practice, however, never to separate a family unless absolutely necessary.

One of the earliest problems arose from the association's limited funds, but once an appeal went out, the response was tremendous. The citizens of New Orleans gave generously, and as news spread throughout the United States, contributions came from every state in the Union. During the first few days the members had doled out medicines and supplies with a sparing hand, realizing that the organization's treasury was in no position to undertake the large-scale spending that apparently was going to be needed. But as donations came pouring in, the members, as one of their number later recorded, "now added comparative luxury to the hovels they visited. The soiled mattresses and bed-clothes, seldom washed or cleaned from indispensably constant use, and reeking with the effluvia consequent thereon, were thrown aside, and replaced with new." Poverty-stricken sufferers, "habituated to sleep upon the floor, . . . were now raised up on cots, freed from a fatal dampness, and open to the ventilation of a higher stratum of atmosphere." The association began supplying them with groceries, meat, cooking utensils, nursing, and "the rich man's privilege of bi-daily visits from a physician." [29] Not only was help extended to the impoverished classes, but in addition it was given to the small shopkeepers, mechanics, and clerks, who were ordinarily independent but who often found themselves in financial straits when sickness struck in the family or removed the wage earner.

Whenever possible, the Howards met daily to report on their activities and to devise better ways of caring for the growing number of sick. As money flowed into the treasury and was dispensed with a liberal hand, the Howards began printing cards valued at from fifty cents to a dollar which the members endorsed and handed to the families of the sick. Tickets for ten cents' worth of ice or twenty cents' worth of beef, for example, or orders for groceries and medicines were also distributed. These tickets or cards endorsed by Howard members were accepted without question by professional men and shopkeepers, and all of them ultimately were redeemed either by the New Orleans city treasurer or by the Howard Association secretary.

The work of the Howards in New Orleans and their counterparts elsewhere—for similar groups existed in nearly every major city—was undoubtedly a factor in awakening the middle classes to the horrible conditions in which the lower-income groups lived. In New Orleans, lawyers, businessmen, clerks, merchants, brokers, and shipowners found themselves visiting miserably crowded hovels and tenements. They saw entire families jammed into single rooms, many of which had no floors save the damp earth. During the torrential showers which characterized the semitropical climate of the Gulf Coast, water flooded into the low-lying houses, carrying with it filth and debris from the streets and gutters. While many of the people they encountered in these situations were brutalized and degraded, the Howards and their co-workers discovered that they were fellow human beings, many of whom had been victims of circumstance.

The same warm human impulses that led the Howards to help the sick were quickened at the sight of their fellow men living in such abject poverty and misery. It was no accident that physicians and ministers were in the forefront of the movement for social legislation during much of the nineteenth century. The nature of their work brought them into intimate contact with impoverishment and degradation. These were not abstractions which could be explained on purely theoretical grounds, but rather desperate and immediate problems involving human lives. Theologians might blandly equate poverty with sinfulness and the will of God; and economists, political thinkers, and successful businessmen could rationalize it on the basis of Ricardo's "Iron Law of Wages" or the Malthusian thesis on population, both of which assumed that poverty for many was a more or less immutable law. But to those physicians and ministers who worked with the poor, the brutal realities of poverty would not permit that it be dealt with as an abstract social question.

William Robinson recorded that his district was one inhabited by a "different and better class of emigrants than any other," yet his descriptions of some of the places he visited only make one wonder what conditions must have been like in the poorer areas. He mentioned that outhouses were fruitful sources of disease and said of the living quarters: "In rooms eighteen feet square there were at least twelve cots, so close together that one man could not pass another. In some the bedding was dirty, the musquito-netting [sic] filthy, the floors spotted with offensiveness, and an atmosphere correspondingly tainted." [30] In another instance he mentioned being called to a yellow fever case in an old two-story building with about twenty-four rooms, each of which, he said, was occupied by four or five tenants. As the fever spread through the building, it became a miniature hospital, and three nurses, "with the assistance of the able occupants, divided their time among the sick." [31]

Robinson started his work in the middle of July, and by the second week he already had sixty cases under his charge, plus many others whom he had sent to the hospitals and infirmaries and for whom he still remained responsible. In the nineteenth century—and well into the twentieth—a doctor was not summoned unless the patient was seriously ill, and this caused the Howards to lose many of their charges. Robinson wrote that frequently he was not sent for until "the disease had had too long a hold to be manageable." The victims were then too ill to be moved to a hospital, and all that could be done was "to follow closely the prescriptions of the physician, to strip death of its precursory agonies, and to hand in, a few hours after, the name of the deceased to the commissary for interment." Every day Howard members would find notes on the slates posted at their homes: "A man dead at No. __ Street; please bury him." Not infrequently corpses lay unattended for a day or more, either because the neighbors were unaware of the tragedy or were in no condition to do anything about it. In the hot, humid climate of New Orleans, putrefaction soon set in, and the foul odor emanating from the deathbed was often the first indication of the grim fact.[32]

To be a member of the Howard Association and work directly with the sick and dying required genuine human sympathy, high moral character, and a strong stomach. Over and above the fact that most of the cases with whom the Howards dealt lived in the crowded, fetid slums, yellow fever itself was a frightful disease. The inability of the physicians to explain its causative factor or even the means by which it spread added the fearful element of the unknown—but more than this, the appearance of its victims was truly a shocking sight. The Reverend Theodore Clapp, founder of Unitarianism in New Orleans and pastor of the Church of the Messiah (Dr. Clapp preferred its popular name, "The Strangers' Church" of New Orleans), spent over thirty years in the city and won enduring fame by remaining at his post during the successive epidemics of yellow fever and Asiatic cholera—in truth serving as his brother's keeper.

Dr. Clapp, at that time the oldest resident minister in New Orleans, had come from Massachusetts in 1822 to assume charge of the First Presbyterian Church. A strong, forceful individual with an inquiring mind, he had come under the influence of William Ellery Channing and his disciples while in theological training. During his early years in New Orleans, as he was formulating his religious philosophy, Dr. Clapp gradually moved in the direction of Unitarianism. His concept of predestination and his views on infant damnation soon brought him into conflict with the orthodox Presbyterians, and after several tumultuous years he was finally tried for heresy and cast out of the Mississippi Synod of the Presbyterian Church. He was so strong and forceful a speaker and so winning a personality that when the crisis came, the majority of his congregation elected to stay with him, and the synod found it had lost both congregation and church.[33]

He had witnessed innumerable deathbed scenes, many of which he described in his *Autobiography* written shortly after his retirement in 1856. Although he was given to the florid prose of his day, he had a sharp eye for detail and a feeling for rhetoric. "Often I have met and shook hands with some blooming, handsome young man today," he wrote, "and in a few hours afterwards, I have been called to see him in the black vomit, with profuse hemorrhages from the mouth, nose, ears, eyes, and even the toes; the eyes prominent, glistening, yellow, and staring; the face discolored with orange color and dusky red." [34] Even death seemed to bring no relief to the yellow fever victim. Witness Dr. Clapp's description: "The physiognomy of the yellow fever corpse is usually sad, sullen, and perturbed; the countenance dark, mottled, livid, swollen, and stained with blood and black vomit; the veins of the face and whole body become distended, and look as if they were going to burst; and though the heart has ceased to beat, the circulation of the blood sometimes continues for hours, quite as active as in life." [35] Farfetched as this latter statement was, in the warm climate of Louisiana the temperature of yellow fever patients occasionally increased after death. A series of experiments by Dr. Bennet Dowler in the 1850's demonstrated this point clearly, and Dowler also noted the tendency of yellow fever cadavers to bleed rather profusely even an hour or more after death. The probable explanation is that the high temperatures prevented the blood from clotting, though quite obviously Dr. Clapp was mistaken in claiming that it continued to circulate.

The month of June had ended on a fairly optimistic note, with only a few undertones of uneasiness; the end of the black month of July was in sharp contrast. For the week ending July 2, the deaths from yellow fever totaled 25; four weeks later the yellow fever death toll for the week ending July 30 was 555. On this same day the *Bee* recorded 105 burials in the city's cemeteries during the preceding twenty-four hours, of which 78 were attributed to yellow fever.[36] On July 31 Charity Hospital reported that in the past week 602 patients had been admitted and 246 had died (231 from yellow fever). In commenting on these figures, the *Delta* noted that only 37 percent of the yellow fever patients in Charity Hospital were recovering, and explained the high fatality rate on the basis that most of the victims were newly arrived immigrants who had neglected to seek medical care until it was too late. The Irish and Germans, the paper stated, "look upon the Hospital as the last place they would go to" and resort to it only when all hope is lost.[37] Already economic activity was nearly halted, and the tolling of bells mingled with the slow clumping of horses' hooves and the rattling of wheels on cobblestones as hearses and wagons bore coffins toward the city's cemeteries. The only brisk movements to be seen came from the physicians, the ministers, and the Howard Association members hurrying through their crowded days.

As July closed, the cemeteries were becoming the busiest places in town. The overworked sextons and gravediggers soon found the situation getting beyond control. At first, by working far into the night, they had managed to clear the graveyards each day, but with the interments numbering over one hundred daily, coffins began to accumulate. The opening days of August were to witness some of the grimmest scenes in the long and colorful history of New Orleans.

CHAPTER V

Endless Funeral Processions

On AUGUST 1 Dr. A. F. Axson summed up the events of the preceding four weeks and gave his readers little reason for hope. "The twenty-eight days in July," he wrote, "of which our record is a faithful and frightful picture, show a gain, incalculable by PER CENTUMS, of mortality by the yellow fever." There had been 46 deaths in the five weeks ending July 2; the next four weeks had seen 1,387 deaths from yellow fever. After pointing to the ignorance, intemperance, and miserable sanitary conditions of the poor, Dr. Axson declared: "It lightens not the responsibility nor abates the terrors of the wide devastation around us to know that of 1,387 human beings who perished in our midst, ninety-nine of every hundred dying, were of our poor and foreign population. Let them be who and what they may, the hundreds who die daily point a fearful truth of which we cannot be too soon or too consciously impressed. They speak out in voices from numberless graves of the utter neglect and criminal remisness [sic] of those put in authority over us. . . ." [1]

But by this date the newspapers were too preoccupied with the mounting death toll to worry about what had been done or what should be done in the future. On August 1 the *Delta* dolefully reported 880 burials during the previous week, 692 the result of yellow fever. Earlier, the journal wrote, it had been assumed that the physicians could check the disease, but it was now evident that their efforts were of little avail. In a tone of discouragement which belied its assertion, the newspaper concluded: "We still have confidence that the worst day has arrived, and pray our readers to have patience for a few days, when we hope to be able to announce the gratifying fact of its rapid decline." [2] The *Bee* was no more encouraging. An editorial headed, "The Fever," began: "The bills of mortality tell their own story—and a frightful one it is." The number of deaths were increasing daily and the epidemic seemed to be widening its field of operations. The only consolation, the editorial said, was the knowledge that yellow fever epidemics follow a standard pattern, usually running their course in six to nine weeks. The presence of the epidemic in New Orleans from the beginning of July made it logical to assume that it would disappear around the end of August. If for no other reason, the editor added, "a want of fuel" would terminate the outbreak. Unfortunately, the editor of the *Bee* greatly underestimated the available "fuel." [3]

The Howard Association had already given aid to over 900 cases of yellow fever. As of July 30, they had discharged 238 patients as cured, had buried another 187, and were caring for 499. With the case fatality rate running around 40 percent, it was little wonder that the disease struck terror into the hearts of the unacclimated. For those residents who thought that a death toll of 100 per day marked the peak of the epidemic, developments in August proved a rude shock. During the first six days the daily number of deaths ranged from 128 to a high of 194 on August 6. [4]

On the face of it, one might expect to see signs of panic and of breakdown. The City Council had abdicated its function, trade and commerce had halted, and the care of the sick was rapidly becoming a major undertaking. Yet a casual reading of the newspapers gives little indication of the desperate conditions within the city. The newspapers, other than publishing the daily cemetery returns and an occasional editorial on the fever, gave an impression of complete normality. Their editorial columns were concerned with local and national politics, foreign affairs, and business matters. Fraternal, benevolent, military, business, and social groups, judging from the newspaper announcements, continued to hold their regular meetings. The advertising columns gave little indication of the growing crisis. Occasional advertisements or news items mentioned cures or preventives against yellow fever, but these were unobtrusive in the long columns of commercial notices. Probably the most consistent reminders of the outbreak were the announcements from the Howard Association. For example, Mr. Ricardo, the secretary, published a statement notifying "all Druggists and other persons having bills against the Howard Association" to present them to him for payment. [5] Almost all the journals carried lists of Howard members, physicians, druggists, and others connected with the organization to whom the sick might apply, but even these brief notices were eclipsed by advertisements for the sale of dry goods, slaves, tobacco, real estate, and other miscellaneous articles. Surprisingly the apothecaries made little effort to take advantage of the crisis, and only an occasional advertisement specifically mentioned yellow fever as, for example, that of F. Clavel, "Druggist and Chemist" located at 150 Old Levee, between Ursuline and Hospital streets, who headed his list of drugs, "Preservatives against Yellow Fever." Among these purported preventives were Raspell's Sedative Water, Seidlitz Water, Labarraque's Chloride of Soda, "purging Lemonade," and "saturated solution of Chloride of Lime." [6]

More significant from the standpoint of revealing the growing crisis was the steady increase in the announcements of meetings of benevolent, charitable, and social organizations. For example, on August 3 the names and addresses of the members of the "Special Relief Committee of Jackson Fire Co. No. 18" were published in the *Delta*. Immediately below this item was another stating that the "Order of the Lone Star" would hold its regular meetings on the second and fourth Mondays of each month. Following this notice was one announcing that the "Masonic Board of Relief" would meet at 11 A.M. every Sunday morning in the office of the grand secretary in the Grand Lodge Hall on the corner of Perdido and St. Charles streets.[7] In the succeeding days many other groups, such as the Louisiana Grays and the New Orleans Typographical Union, began setting up relief committees. In fact by the end of the first week in August, the functioning of official and unofficial relief committees was a major business in the city.[8]

On August 4 the Grand Jury for New Orleans issued a report in which it took up a number of local matters, including the sale of liquor and lottery tickets and the conditions of the orphan asylums and other city institutions. Apropos the yellow fever, the report declared: "We approach the subject of health with painful emotions." Without attempting to decide upon the origin of the disease, the report continued, we believe that the atrocious sanitary condition of the city is largely responsible for intensifying the outbreak. After listing the many abuses—dead animals, garbage, filth, and so forth—the grand jury said: "It is to these sources that we trace the prevalence of disease, and not to our geographical position or climate." In summing up its conclusions, the grand jury asserted: "The entire health or sanitary system is radically wrong." [9]

On this same day one of the papers editorialized in an unusually pessimistic fashion upon the course of the outbreak. After pointing out that the Board of Health reports showed no lessening of the mounting toll of deaths, the editor stated: "It seems impossible that this frightful havoc can continue much longer." After having lived twenty-one years in New Orleans, he wrote, "we have never witnessed so many deaths per day from the disease. Let any one cooly reflect that the Fever is killing two percent of the unacclimated population every week, that is from eight to nine hundred out of forty or fifty thousand—and then calculate how long it would take to annihilate this class of our inhabitants." [10] The only possible ray of hope lay in the consideration that if the eight or nine hundred deaths each week represented four to five thousand new cases, in from seven to ten weeks every unacclimated person in the city would have had the fever. Most would survive and thereby become immune. The intensity of the outbreak is shown by the editor's estimate that only about one fifth of the city's inhabitants would pass through the epidemic unscathed. By implication, approximately 80 percent were expected to fall sick!

As the deaths continued their remorseless climb, the newspapers began to sound an ominous tone. On August 8, when the yellow fever deaths had reached two hundred per day, a newspaper writer declared that it seemed impossible "that this fearful ratio can long continue. . . . So many thousands have been attacked; so many hundreds have perished," the editorial stated, ". . . that it is difficult even now to understand where the fever finds its victims. Our streets are deserted—the pavement echoes the footfall of the casual wayfarer—gloom, silence and desolation overspread the city." More than half the resident population, the paper went on, has fled from the pestilence, but "in the obscure quarters of the city . . . there are still throngs of the laboring classes, in whose squalid dwellings disease loves to linger, and who furnish hecatombs to glut the pestilence." By way of consoling its readers, who presumably did not live in squalor, the editorial added: "One of the faculty, who enjoys a very extensive practice, assures us that if subjected to active treatment, within the twenty-four hours following indisposition, Yellow Fever is far more easily manageable than many other varieties of fever, which are not considered dangerous." [11]

The special knowledge which enabled this particular physician to deal so easily with yellow fever was evidently not shared by his professional colleagues. Just a few days earlier the *New Orleans Monthly Medical Register* had published obituaries of two young doctors, victims of yellow fever. One of them, Dr. A. R. Nye, was a graduate of the medical department of the University of Louisiana in New Orleans, certainly the one school in the United States where presumably he would have learned to deal with yellow fever. As a matter of fact, he had learned the lessons of his preceptors in New Orleans so well that he had been chosen as class orator at his graduation, an event which preceded his death by only a few months. The other victim was a young Swedish physician who had come just recently to the United States. Since many southern medical men were already beginning to assert that southern medical practice and southern diseases were distinct from those of the more northerly regions, and young Dr. Jacobson was a newcomer, his death seemed readily understandable.[12] On August 2 the news editor of the *Daily Crescent* also succumbed to the prevailing epidemic.[13] He, too, was a newcomer, but presumably, like the two young physicians, had been given adequate medical care. So it was quite evident from the death notices appearing with greater frequency in the daily columns that deaths were occurring among the "better people." The only question is whether the editors of the newspapers indulged in wishful thinking in denying this fact or whether they felt it a responsibility of the press to buoy up public morale.

With public and private hospitals overflowing, the Board of Health soon found it necessary to establish temporary yellow fever infirmaries. On August 2 it was announced that three hospitals had been opened "for the reception of the destitute sick." [14] Applications for admission to these institutions could be signed by any member of the Common Council, the Board of Health, or the Howard Association. An even more grim reminder of the growing threat was the opening of two asylums "for the temporary reception of orphan children that may come under the charge of this Board or the Howard Association." [15] Another group suffering from the effect of the outbreak was described as "that large number of females, who have, heretofore, had some male relative or friend to protect them, [and] are now friendless and homeless. . . ." Mr. C. K. O'Hara was reported to have kindly offered his services on behalf of "these poor creatures, and will no doubt do all he can to alleviate their many wants." [16]

On Sunday morning, August 7, the *Picayune* published the weekly death toll, one which showed that 194 persons had died of yellow fever the previous day. In commenting, the paper asserted that changes in the atmosphere were considered the most newsworthy of all items since the epidemic seemed to fluctuate with the thermometer. The correlation between deaths and the weather, however, was not one on which any sort of general agreement could be reached. For some observers the ratio between temperature and deaths was a direct one; *i.e.*, the deaths increased with the temperature. The *Picayune* had a different idea, for it declared that the 194 deaths recorded on Saturday "may be safely ascribed to the COLD NORTH WIND which blew since the day before yesterday." On Monday, August 8, one of the editors wrote despondently, "It has rained, rained, rained, day after day, and day after day for so long that our memory hardly runneth to the contrary." It had been hoped that the cool weather on the previous Friday and Saturday would have ended "our dull, dreary, wet weather; but this hope faded yesterday." He concluded that "the prospect for the sick is still more dreary on this account." [17]

It was at this discouraging moment that a crisis broke in the cemeteries which was to blacken the name of New Orleans and give the impression that its citizens were both irresponsible and callous. With burials close to two hundred per day, it was not to be wondered that disordered conditions should arise in the cemeteries. This situation was especially true in the Fourth District Cemetery to which the bodies of the impoverished were taken. All of the newspapers expressed disgust and indignation, but the *Delta* was the first to draw attention to the problem. On August 8 it published an editorial entitled "Horrible Spectacle" in which it noted that the municipal carts were engaged daily in collecting the coffins of the poor and depositing them in the Fourth District Cemetery. Here they were buried in shallow graves ranging from eighteen inches to two feet in depth with only a couple of inches of dirt thrown over the coffins. On the preceding Friday seventy-one bodies had arrived at the cemetery, where only six men were employed in digging graves. The gravediggers were already getting behind in their work when some of the men, unable to stand the hard work, the heat, the stench, and the loathsome nature of the task, decided to quit. Some forty coffins were left unburied over the weekend.

The result was tragic. As the *Delta* explained, "The action of the sun, through the frail enclosures, produced a rapid decomposition of the bodies, several of which swelled, so as to burst the coffins." Attracted by the unusually violent and offensive effluvia, several citizens in the neighborhood visited the spot, and they subsequently informed the street commissioner and the mayor. The street commissioner was sympathetic but claimed he was unable to secure laborers. Mayor Crossman was reported to have said that the matter "did not fall within his line of duty." The editor, while admitting that from a legal standpoint there was considerable question as to where the responsibility lay, concluded bitterly: "Our city government, on occasions of public emergency and danger, is a mere farce." [18]

The *Picayune* was equally outraged over the situation. Its editor declared that coffins were reaching the cemetery at all hours, day and night, and that the foul odors emanating from the putrefying bodies could be detected as far as five blocks from the graveyard. He demanded that the municipal officials offer enough money to attract laborers. If they could not get white men, he said, then they should use Negroes.[19] The following day, August 9, the *Delta* published its classic and oft-quoted editorial, "A Visit to the Cemetery." The author had visited the Fourth District Cemetery to see for himself what conditions were like. En route he learned that the city officials had "ceased to send corpses to this place, in order to give time to bury those which already lay on the ground." As he approached the gates, he was conscious of much activity with carts, wagons, and hearses passing and repassing. "As we passed through the gates, inhaling a most pestilential odor," he wrote, "we noticed a curious exhibition of the careless indifference too characteristic of our people on occasions like this. Before the door of the small house at the gate of the cemetery, we saw several little children engaged in the most joyous merriment, and an old woman vending ice cream to passers-by, who had to hold camphor to their noses to avoid fainting from the odor." [20]

It was a strange contrast, he wrote, "with the gloomy spectacle within. There lay quite a number of coffins of rough, unplaned plank, painted a gloomy black, with myriads of flies hanging around them, and discharging a most repulsive odor." A chain gang of Negroes was rapidly depositing the coffins in trenches, "dug scarcely a foot deep." The white laborers, despite offers of as much as five dollars per hour, had "either died or abandoned the ground." The coffins were piled six at a time into the shallow graves, quick lime was sprinkled over them, and a thin layer of dirt piled on top. Even the Negro slaves could be kept at their grim task only "by liberal and frequent potations of whiskey." By sunset the last of the coffins was buried, thanks to the decision to send no additional bodies to the graveyard until it had been cleared. On viewing the desolate scene, the editor could not help exclaiming: "But what burials they were! To think that in an acre of ground around us, there were not less than four hundred bodies, lying but a few inches below the surface of the ground, in the very first stages of decomposition, deposited there within the last week." [21]

After deploring "the utter want of system or organization" for dealing with such an emergency, the writer praised those city officials who had assumed authority and rectified the situation. In particular, he singled out Mayor Crossman who was at the graveyard, "superintending and hastening the work of interment." Reflecting gloomily upon the bizarre picture he had been witnessing, the editor delicately suggested that, repugnant as it might be to the sensibilities of the citizens, "the Roman custom of burning the dead" might be more suitable for New Orleans.[22]

Even more moving than the ghastly scenes at the cemetery were those enacted on the streets leading to the graveyards. Here could be seen hearses driven by tired Negroes and pulled by toil-worn horses, often without a single mourner; others were followed by the victim's family and friends who, "in their miserable, woe-begone countenances, exhibited real distress." For sheer tragedy, the sight of the corporation carts driven by rough, blasphemous cartmen seated upon one end of the three coffins usually borne by each cart, was scarcely to be equalled. Although mourners rarely followed the corpses of the destitute and forlorn poor "who had no friends to mourn for them," occasionally the pathetic remnants of a family could be seen in the wake of the carts. The writer described one case of a corporation wagon driven by a young boy who urged on his tired horse with oaths and blows. "Behind the cart, in the blazing sun, walked a girl, nearly grown, clad in an old mourning dress, and leading by the hand a little boy, ten or twelve years of age. They were all that were left of a family, which, last week, numbered some half a dozen members; this was their father they were accompanying to the grave." When the writer attempted to dissuade them from making the 2-mile journey to the cemetery, all he could elicit was "the plaintive cry: 'Mon pauvre père! mon pauvre père!' " [23]

The rich nineteenth-century rhetoric of the *Delta* was eminently suitable for describing the horror scenes of the New Orleans epidemics, but compared with that of the *Crescent*, the *Delta* style seems sparse and dry. On Thursday morning, August 11, under the title "Down Among the Dead Men," a reporter for the *Crescent* pulled out all stops of his newspaper organ. Since his readers were all too familiar with what he had to say, one cannot doubt his graphic depiction of the scenes in New Orleans, but the story lost nothing in the telling. In every street he found long processions "tramping to the music of funeral marches. . . ." The faces of plodding passersby wore "lines of anxiety and grief, and many a door was festooned with black and white hangings, the voiceless witnesses of wailing and of sorrow." He contrasted the long corteges of the wealthy, with their nodding plumes and prancing horses, and the martial funerals of the citizen-soldiers with that of the pauper, "trundled to his long home on a ricketty cart" while the driver with careless oaths urged his mule or spavined horse to a trot, "making haste with another morsel contributed to the grand banquet of death." Above the mournful tolling of the bells in the poorer districts occasionally could be heard "the low wail of a mother for the child of her affections, while from the corner opposite burst the song of some low bacchanal, mingling ribaldry with sentiment, or swearing a prayer or two as the humor moved him." [24]

The cloudless sunshine above was "but little in keeping with the black melancholy that enveloped all below. Out along the highways that lead to the cities of the dead, and still the tramp of funeral crowds knew no cessation. Up rolled the volumes of dust from the busy roads, and the plumes of the death carriages nodded in seeming sympathy to the swaying cypresses of the swamp, enveloped in their dun appareling [sic] of weeping moss—fit garniture for such a scene." As the hearses, carriages, and wagons massed near the cemeteries the "vulgar teamsters, as they jostled each other in the press, mingled the coarse jest with the ribald oath; no sound but of profane malediction and of riotous mirth, the clang of whip thongs and the rattle of wheels." Inside the cemeteries the rotting corpses "were piled by fifties, exposed to the heat of the sun, swollen with corruption, bursting their coffin lids, and sundering as if by physical effort, the ligaments that bound their hands and feet, and extending their rigid limbs in every outré attitude. What a feast of horrors!" [25]

Outside the graveyards were "old and withered crones and fat huckster women, fretting in their own grease, dispensing ice creams and confections, and brushing away, with brooms made of bushes, the green bottle-flies that hovered on their merchandise, and that anon buzzed away to drink dainty inhalations from the green and festering corpses. Mammon at the gates was making thrift outside by the hands of his black and sweating minions . . . while within, the 'King of Terrors' held his Saturnalia, with a crowd of stolid laborers. . . ." These men, grown used to "the scent of dissolution," had lost all human sympathy, and as they dug into the fetid earth under the broiling sun, their mattocks or spades would occasionally strike a skull or large bone, causing them to curse as they hurled it aside. The coffins of infants and children were often separated from those of their parents in order to fill up spaces in the mass graves between the larger coffins. Gathered in the graveyards were crowds of people—many wearing bags of camphor and spices on their noses—who came simply "to look on and contemplate the vast congregation of the dead." Thus, the observer wrote, the day wears on until night "draws the curtain." Even then there was no relief, for the work was carried on far into the night under the fitful gleam of torches and lanterns.[26]

Eleven thousand persons died in the epidemic which swept New Orleans in the summer of 1853. The task of burying the dead was carried on far into the night under the fitful gleam of torches and lanterns.

The editorials and stories in the New Orleans papers were quickly picked up by other journals and reported throughout the United States, creating an impression of complete chaos and anarchy in the Crescent City. The awful situation was the result of circumstances which were frequently present in many other cities at this date; but the hot climate of New Orleans, by quickening the putrefaction, greatly intensified the problem. In the deadly summer months the graveyards of New Orleans were scarcely equipped to handle over 100 burials daily, and on the Saturday before the exposé no less than 194 deaths were recorded.

In order to simplify administrative procedure the city had assigned pauper burials to one particular cemetery, paying the sexton at the Lafayette Cemetery the sum of one dollar per burial. The sexton, in turn, had traditionally paid twenty cents per grave to the gravediggers, and he refused to increase his payments as conditions in the graveyard steadily worsened. Moreover, at one of the other graveyards, where a number of graves had already been dug, the impassable condition of the street leading to the entrance forced the hearses to seek elsewhere for a burial site. It was this combination of circumstances which aroused the public and led to action on the part of the city officials.[27]

All in all, the mayor acted firmly and decisively once the matter was drawn to his attention. He promptly dispatched a chain gang of Negro convicts to assist in the burials at Lafayette Cemetery and ordered that bodies to be buried at city expense be distributed to the other cemeteries until the Lafayette situation was cleared up. Alderman Kursheedt, who was chairman of the Board of Health cemetery committee, reported on August 8 that he had visited Lafayette shortly after the mayor had taken action and discovered that one of the police officers was about to take the chain gang away. Kursheedt had ordered the Negro convicts to remain at the cemetery and had issued an appeal to all citizens to send him some gravediggers, offering to pay five dollars per hour and to supply food and drink until all the bodies were buried. Orders had also been issued for three hundred loads of dirt "to be placed over the graves that were insufficient depth, from having been hastily dug," and the street commissioner had been instructed henceforth to distribute the bodies more evenly among the various graveyards. Mr. Kursheedt further proposed to the Board of Health that the police chief be requested to detail three policemen from each district to see that all public vehicles were promptly removed as soon as the interments were finished so that the roads "remain unobstructed and clear for the admission of funeral processions." [28]

Thus, on Monday, August 8, the graveyard conditions which had led to the outcry and occasioned the newspaper editorials were actually well in hand, and provision had been made to prevent a recurrence of the dreadful events of the previous weekend. Although the death toll per day was to climb much higher before the epidemic reached its peak, never again were these conditions to be repeated. Deficient as the municipal officers had been in anticipating this crisis, Mayor Crossman and his Board of Health had unhesitatingly swung into action to remedy the situation.

By this time the damage was done, and as news of the ever-mounting number of deaths from yellow fever spread throughout the country, it was difficult for those unaware of true conditions not to believe the worst about New Orleans. For many years afterwards New Orleans was looked upon as a city whose governing officials flagrantly neglected their duty and whose citizens were brutalized and devoid of all human compassion. In reality, the city administration, despite the failures of its members, rose to meet the crisis in a far better fashion than did civic officials in most American cities during these years. Moreover, the percentage of middle and upper class citizens in New Orleans who assumed the responsibilities of brotherhood was almost unprecedented. They were not content with merely supplying financial and moral support for the impoverished sick but went into wretched hovels and tenements and actually nursed the occupants back to health. The New Orleans newspapers awakened the city's conscience and undoubtedly contributed to correcting abuses, but, alas for New Orleans, their effect upon public opinion outside the city was almost disastrous.

The black weekend of August 6 marks one of the low points of the crisis-ridden summer of 1853, but it was no turning point in the epidemic onslaught. Even as the city was amending conditions in the graveyards, the yellow fever was pressing its attack more fiercely. On Monday, August 8, a total of 219 deaths was recorded, of which 187 were ascribed to the fever. For the rest of the week the deaths did not fall below 200 per day, and when the score was totaled the following Sunday no less than 1,526 New Orleanians had perished.[29] Increasingly the newspapers published notices from various social and charitable groups announcing important business meetings. Irish, German, and French nationality organizations were actively giving aid to their fellow countrymen. Volunteer firemen and military associations, fraternal and religious groups, and churches of all denominations were engaged in the ceaseless task of caring for the sick and dying. As news of the city's plight spread, generous citizens from all parts of the United States responded with donations of money, food, medicines, and hospital supplies. From cities as far away as Boston and New York contributions came pouring in to the Howard Association. Young physicians also arrived in New Orleans to help. Some were undoubtedly motivated by a chance to try their skill against what was probably the most dreaded disease of its day; some may have hoped to win fame and fortune in short order; but the greater majority were responding to the cries of suffering humanity. In 1853 the risks incident to going to New Orleans in the midst of a yellow fever epidemic were far too great to appeal to calculating men.

Meanwhile the long hot days and insufferably humid nights of August were bearing down on the city, making the sickrooms even more fetid and unbearable. The newspapers, no longer restricted by a self-imposed censorship, now openly discussed the omnipresent sickness. In commenting upon the annual parade of Fire Company No. 18, which had been held to the accompaniment of the usual martial music, the *Delta* noted that there had been much criticism of the group for holding its celebration in a time of such mourning. The editor added, however, that he was aware that arrangements had been made a month earlier, when no one expected the epidemic to become so virulent. He went on to suggest that the firemen, military companies, and other organizations refrain from holding elaborate funerals which served only as reminders of the terrible mortality. It would be far better, he thought, to accompany the body to the cemetery with only a small detachment of acclimated men. Not only was public morale adversely affected by constant funeral processions marching through the streets, but also yellow fever patients suffered deleterious effects. He had heard many physicians declare that those who participated in these sad affairs were needlessly exposing themselves to the disease, and he asked: "Do not these mid-day processions add largely to the victims of the pestilence?" [30]

The lead editorial in this same newspaper expressed the shocked amazement which even the oldest inhabitants exhibited in the face of the unprecedented calamity: "Still onward stalks the dreadful pestilence through our afflicted city. Every minute seems to give it strength and vigor. Increased victims appear to sharpen rather than glut its savage appetite. It leaps over all barriers, and spurns all opposition." No longer did this awful distemper restrict itself to the "lower classes"—now the rich and poor, the prudent and imprudent, the virtuous and the vicious, "all alike, fall before the remorseless sickle of this great destroyer, and are gathered into one common harvest of death." Only about two weeks before, the *Delta* had been criticized for announcing the epidemic and now the pestilence has become "one of the most destructive, malignant and distressing which ever fell upon a people." Earlier it had been calculated that after deducting the number of native citizens and those acclimated, some thirty thousand residents were still potential victims of yellow fever. Of this number, the editorial continued," at least three thousand have already been buried, and every day adds two hundred more to the ghastly record." If the epidemic raged at this rate for the rest of the month, the number of victims would reach five thousand by September 1, the date, he said, when an epidemic ordinarily would just be reaching its peak. There had been days in previous epidemics when the death toll on individual days had been higher than any so far in this outbreak, "but on no other occasion has the aggregate weekly mortality been as large, nor the progress of the disease so steady, regular, and unbroken! What is the worst aspect of these facts is, that the season for the prevalence of the epidemic has barely commenced." After mentioning that many patients were recovering from the fever, the editor took a sly dig at the medical profession. "Indeed," he wrote, "it would appear that the thousands, who have already died could not have had the advantage of medical attendance, as the physicians all declare that they have lost no cases! It is wonderful how successful they are, considering the vast amount of mortality!" Two columns over from the editorial Dr. J. C. Simonds reported for the Board of Health that the official burials for the previous day totaled 229, a grim footnote attesting to the inability of the medical profession to stem the rising epidemic tide.[31]

New Orleans was well supplied with a variety of newspapers representing almost every shade of political opinion. Although they had been loud in their denunciation of the city fathers at the beginning of the epidemic, the attitude of the editors became calmer, more reasonable and objective. As the pestilence rolled inexorably through New Orleans, each week exacting a heavier toll, the newspaper columns presented a fairly accurate picture of events in the city. For example, when an indignant citizen wrote to one of the newspapers bitterly excoriating the City Council for not being at hand to face the crisis, the *Delta* reproved the writer and appealed for unity and harmony. In reply to this citizen's demand that the council remain in session to appropriate enough money to have all the streets cleaned, it was pointed out that a good part of the original $10,000 appropriated in July was still unspent. It was all very well, the editor said, to demand that the streets be cleaned, but where could one find laborers? The street commissioner had been given complete authority in this respect and had employed all available workers. The editor agreed with the citizen that for twenty years past the city had neglected its streets, but no matter how much money was appropriated the streets could still not be brought into a sanitary condition in the midst of a major epidemic.[32]

In any event, were the streets of New Orleans "paved with marble, and as clean as Rotterdam, it would not arrest the present awful march of the pestilence. Besides," the editor went on, "if our people are employed in cleaning the streets and fumigating yards, what is to become of the sick, the dying, the dead—whom there are not people to nurse and bury? These duties engage all the attention of that portion of our population which is not liable to the epidemic." He rejoiced that instead of wrangling about near-useless laws, the council members were employed much more beneficially in their private capacities "in attending the sick, in aiding the poor, and in burying the dead." His editorial concluded by appealing for calmness and a reasonable approach: "Let each man in his sphere strive to ameliorate the distress around him without working himself into an unseemly passion against his neighbors. To indulge in partisan feelings, such as have been manifested on this occasion, appears to us, as unseemly and improper as those exhibitions of brutal passions which have disgraced the neighborhoods of some of our Cemeteries." [33]

On Monday, August 15, the *Bee*, in noting that fifteen hundred residents had died during the preceding seven days, stated with quiet despair: "The list of interments for the past week is the best evidence one can offer of the terrible mortality of the Fever." It had been reported by the physicians that more yellow fever patients were recovering, and the paper hoped that this might indicate that the worst was over. In the meantime public and private benevolence was exerting itself to the utmost to bring relief to the poor victims of the sickness. Contributions from many distant cities and towns, combined with generous donations from Louisiana citizens, were enabling the Howard Association members "to extend still further the sphere of their usefullness, and to carry comfort, hope and succor to the lowly dwellings of the indigent and suffering." [34]

By August 15 everyone who could afford to leave New Orleans had fled; despite the shortage of laborers, the worst filth and debris had been cleaned from the streets and lime generously sprinkled in all public places. Collectively and individually the town's physicians had advised the people how best to escape infection and what to do in the event of sickness. For those whose work compelled them to be abroad, nose bags filled with aromatic spices or cloths soaked in vinegar were in common use. The clothing and bed linens of those who died were either burned or subjected to rigorous washing and fumigation. In the meantime physicians were desperately trying every conceivable remedy, ranging from huge and heroic doses of calomel and quinine and massive blood-letting to the opposite treatment of the homeopathic doctors who were convinced that the value of drugs lay in an inverse ratio to the amount prescribed—a theory which left the cure of the patient largely in the hands of nature.

Despite everything that was done in the way of prevention and cure, the number of deaths continued its remorseless climb. Blindly searching for some means to break the grip of pestilence, on Thursday, August 18, Mayor Crossman, on the advice of the Board of Health, ordered the firing of cannon at sunrise and sunset in various sections of the city. The 6-pound cannon of one of the artillery companies were set up in public squares and a total of fifty shots fired twice daily. As a further means of purifying the air, barrels of tar were placed on the street corners and burned during the night. Precisely what effect the roaring of the cannon and the leaping flames from the tar barrels must have had upon the frightened people is difficult to say, but the acrid smell of burnt gunpowder and the black smoke from the tar must have made the hot blanket of moist air which had settled over New Orleans in that unusually wet summer even more oppressive than usual. The newspaper reaction was generally skeptical, with most of the editors conceding that probably little good would result but that certainly there would be no harm. The *Bee*, in reporting the firing of the cannon, declared it to be a waste of gunpowder: "Such expedients have been frequently tried, but we never yet heard of them doing any good." [35] The *Picayune* on the same morning expressed what was probably a more general view—that while firing cannon might be ineffective, it would at least serve to encourage some of the people.[36]

A Mr. Thomas J. Spear wrote to one of the newspapers suggesting a refinement of the cannon-firing practice which he believed would make it far more efficacious. He recommended that one or two pounds of gunpowder be placed in the center and at the four corners of each square within the city. At about 7:30 A.M., "which is about the time that the miasma begins to rise from the earth," the gunpowder was to be touched off, as simultaneously as possible, and thus in one fell swoop the air of the city would be thoroughly cleansed. It was a well-known fact that smoke was a great purifier of the air, he declared, and he was confident that several day's trial of his method would bring an end to the epidemic.[37]

Regrettably for the cause of science, Mr. Spear's suggestion came to nought. The flashing and thundering of the cannon, far from reassuring the townspeople, merely heightened the apprehensions of the well and worsened the condition of those seriously ill with the fever. According to reports, many patients were thrown into convulsions by the sound of the guns, and the resulting protests led Mayor Crossman to discontinue the gunfire after two days. The practice of burning tar, however, was continued, and the combined flames and smoke from hundreds of tar barrels scattered throughout the streets and cemeteries crowned the city with a pall of smoke in the daytime and created an eerie glow at night. An incidental result of burning tar in the cemeteries was a rumor to the effect that the shortage of gravediggers had compelled the city to burn the bodies of yellow fever victims.[38] The rumor was picked up by out-of-town newspapers and given widespread credence, much to the disgust of the New Orleans newspapers. In the paradoxical morality of the Victorian Age, the poor could be worked to death in firetrap buildings and dangerous factories; they could die of malnutrition and disease in filthy, crowded hovels; or they might drop off like flies in the great epidemics with only a few voices raised in their behalf—but, once dead, they could be reasonably assured of Christian burial!

CHAPTER VI

The Black Day

SATURDAY, AUGUST 20, was a gloomy day. The cannons no longer roared but the acrid smell of gunpowder and tar hung heavy over the town. At all major intersections, burning tar barrels cast their thick, black, oily smoke skyward, where the clouds "hung like a funeral pall over the city, as if they were nailed to the sky. . . ." A physician recorded that he was thankful he could no longer hear "the booming of the cannon like a death signal falling suddenly upon the ear. . . ." The awful sound, he wrote, "sent a thrill of terror to my very vitals, and I could feel my heart beat quicker and my brain throb with emotion, despite all my philosophy." It seemed "that Death himself was bombarding the city" and that every discharge of his cannons was sending "hundreds of poor creatures to their graves. . . ." [1]

The optimism that had filled the newspapers during the early weeks of the outbreak had gradually faded away in the face of the appalling statistics published daily by the Board of Health. The editor of the *Bee* on this Saturday gloomily noted that the "tables of mortality continue to present a frightful record." The Board of Health had reported 234 burials in the preceding twenty-four hours, not counting another 8 interments in the Hebrew Cemetery. "When and where will the fever end?" exclaimed the editor. Most of the unacclimated residents had either fled, died, or recovered from the fever, yet the epidemic continued to claim more and more victims and to "baffle all reasoning founded upon past experience." [2]

The *Price-Current*, a local business journal, commented this Saturday upon the remarkable dullness of the markets. Virtually no produce was arriving from the interior, and in any case there were few people available to handle it, "so completely has the fatal epidemic now running its course impeded and deranged all commercial calculations." The prostration of business, brought about by "the claims of the sick upon their friends," was so great that the leading commercial houses were now closing at 3 P.M. each day. Accentuating the gravity of the situation was an announcement in the newspapers that the Howard Association was opening up four new hospitals. In the period from August 1 to August 20, four temporary hospitals had been established by the Board of Health, since Charity and the private hospitals were filled to overflowing. In addition, the Howard Association had opened several convalescent hospitals and three orphanages. One of the last of these, which was opened on August 20, was a combined hospital and orphanage set up in the Washington Schoolhouse on Magazine Street near the corner of Robin.[3]

Despite the fact that the hospitals were established under the most difficult and trying circumstances, they were well managed and in surprisingly good condition. The *Delta* that weekend carried a detailed account of one of Mayor Crossman's tours of the city's various institutions. At Infirmary No. 1, on Hevia Street, which was under the direction of Mr. C. H. Lyster, the mayor and his party found conditions too crowded and the ventilation poor. So many bunks were packed into the main rooms that there was scarce space for the nurses to get to the patients. The building, however, was scrupulously clean, and the physicians and nurses were paying "the most kind and tender attention . . . to the sick." The paper noted that the infirmary had admitted 242 patients since it had first opened on August 1; of these 80 had died.

Infirmary No. 2, originally the Globe Ballroom, had opened on Tuesday, August 16, with William L. Robinson in charge and Dr. Tricou and Dr. Le Mat serving as house physicians. It was, the newspaper report said, ideally suited as a hospital. The wards for the patients were large, well lighted, and well ventilated; a number of small rooms were available for the nurses, clerks, and assistants. One ward was reserved for the dying, so that those patients who might recover would not be affected by the sight. One of the seven patients in this room died while the mayor was inspecting the infirmary, a circumstance which deeply affected the *Delta* reporter. He commented that segregating the hopeless patients was "a most humane and proper arrangement" for many of those who had recovered had remarked that their worst experience in the hospitals had been "witnessing the throes and agony of the dying around them." [4]

The next stop was at Infirmary No. 3 in the Third District. This hospital, under the care of the Reverend C. W. Whitall and Mr. Vandergrif, was one of the first established and had also been in operation since August 1. So rapidly had it filled that another building had already been commandeered to relieve the pressure. Altogether 247 patients had been admitted; two-thirds of these were Germans, the rest Irish and French. The reporter observed that not "an American has applied for admission as yet."

The last infirmary visited, No. 4 in the Fourth District, was under the care of a Dr. Wren. Here the records had been so "very imperfectly kept" that it was impossible to determine the exact number of admissions, discharges, and deaths. It was thought that around 277 patients had been admitted, nearly all of whom were Germans, and that about 73 of these had died. The rear of the building was used as a temporary asylum for forty-seven children who had lost both parents to the fever. The mayor next visited another temporary orphanage on Julia Street where ninety-seven children were housed. The *Delta* noted that many "of the poor little things were vainly crying for their mothers." In concluding its account, the newspaper observed that Mayor Crossman, who had assumed full charge when the aldermen and assistant aldermen had cravenly abdicated their responsibility, made it a point of visiting all hospitals and orphanages twice daily and always had "a word of kindness and encouragement for the sick and the orphans." [5]

Although it seems that the mounting problems created by the epidemic would have preoccupied all attention, the newspapers still found time to worry about the city's reputation. The facts were bad enough in themselves, but frequently out-of-town newspapers embellished them beyond recognition. The intimate relationship between violence and sex almost guaranteed that overtones of sexual irregularities would creep into accounts of the disaster. Indeed, scarcely a pamphlet was published that did not contain sketches of deathbed scenes in which one or more of the corpses was that of a buxom female with at least one breast exposed. As news of the incredible events in New Orleans gradually spread throughout the country, sensation-seeking writers let their imaginations run wild and conjured up all sorts of immoral scenes; the presence of the stalking figure of Death was supposed to have released all inhibitions. An article in the Charleston *Mercury* on August 16 declared that it was "indeed appalling . . . that mere hopelessness and the incessant presence of death has in a measure banished the virtues of humanity and substituted a reckless and brutal sensuality." The New Orleans editor

Sensation-seeking writers and artists let their imaginations run wild in depicting the horrors of the plague. This sketch was captioned "Family Scene—Yellow Fever in New Orleans, 1853."

who reprinted these words was justly outraged by them. Never, he wrote, was such criticism less justified, for those who remained in New Orleans had consistently displayed "the noblest feelings of nature." [6]

Fortunately the truth was given equally wide circulation, and the New Orleans newspapers deserve some credit for this. As mentioned earlier, once the epidemic struck in full force, the daily journals reported the grisly events faithfully and factually. They did not hesitate to criticize officials or private individuals or to call attention to specific abuses. On the other hand, they were equally generous in praise of those who were doing their utmost to allay the suffering of the sick and impoverished. In spite of an incredibly mounting toll of sickness and death, their pages reflect none of the panic which at times must have affected the citizenry. Pessimism and gloom occasionally tinged the editorials, but the general tone was one of guarded optimism. The editor of the *Delta* undoubtedly derived considerable satisfaction this gloomy weekend in being able to reprint an editorial from the *Philadelphia Ledger* of August 13 commending the New Orleans newspapers upon their attitude in the crisis. The Philadelphia editorial pointed out that northern papers were devoting many columns to detailed reports of the terrible epidemic, whereas the New Orleans papers seemed to pay short attention to it. Other than a daily report of the burials, there was scarcely "a reference to the disease in the editorial columns, and an utter and complete absence of any appearance of alarm and excitement. . . . The Courts are in daily operation," the editorial continued, "the Grand Jury make their presentment, politics are discussed, the markets are as active as usual at this season, steamboats come and go, and the whole aspect of their newspapers is that of a city in the enjoyment of its usual health." This calm, matter-of-fact approach, the editorialist added, had robbed the outbreak of half its terror and helped to reduce its malignancy.[7]

Ironically, while certain newspapers in distant parts of the country were assuming the worst about New Orleans, its citizens were dedicating themselves to the sick and dying. Every newspaper issue in the grim days of August contained announcements from a wide variety of organizations relating to the work of their relief committees. For example, on August 20 a Masonic Lodge offered the Howard Association a building at the corner of Dumaine and St. Claude streets for the use of convalescents. Church leaders, too, without exception threw themselves into the battle. Accusations of deserting their flocks had been levied against some of the Protestant ministers during previous epidemics, but the epidemic of 1853 found all the clergy steadfast in their duties. The Reverend Mr. Whitall of the Seamen's Mission, a Protestant Episcopal minister, was singled out by many observers for his unremitting contributions. His parish was located in one of the poorer districts of the city and brought him in close contact with yellow fever victims from the very onset of the disease.[8]

In general, the majority of the poor were Irish and German immigrants of the Catholic faith, whereas the Protestant churches tended to draw their support from middle and upper class Americans. The rumors about Protestant ministers deserting their congregations undoubtedly arose in part from the practice of many to go north or to travel abroad during the hot summer months. In at least two instances, ministers who had left New Orleans in the summer of 1853 returned immediately upon hearing of the outbreak. The minister of the First Presbyterian Church, the Reverend J. L. Twitchell, who had faithfully remained at his post during thirteen yellow fever seasons, was given a leave of absence by his congregation to visit Europe this tragic summer. While awaiting his ship in New York city, he heard of the yellow fever outbreak and immediately set forth for New Orleans. A brief note in the *Picayune* on August 19 mentioned that he had been delayed by low water on the western rivers but had returned that morning and would preach as usual in his church the following Sunday.[9]

Another minister to return in the midst of the epidemic was the Reverend Theodore Clapp. Throughout the successive epidemics of yellow fever and Asiatic cholera Dr. Clapp had labored on behalf of the sick without regard to their religious affiliation. At a time when religious feeling against Catholicism was still quite strong, Dr. Clapp displayed an unusual degree of Christian tolerance and developed close friendships with some of the priests. His courage and fortitude had shone like a beacon for his fellow ministers whenever pestilences struck their cruel blows at New Orleans. In June of 1853 he had gone with his family to visit relatives in Massachusetts. Like the Reverend Twitchell, he set out for New Orleans immediately upon hearing the bad news, but he encountered delays which prevented him from reaching the city until August 26.[10] Immediately upon his arrival, he began providing both spiritual and physical comfort to the sick and afflicted.

The work of the Catholic priests and sisters with the sick and poor in New Orleans was generally recognized, and none were ever accused of leaving their posts. Although the French aristocracy, or Creoles, were Catholics, impoverished immigrants formed a major part of the Church's flock, and it was these people who bore the brunt of the epidemic on-slaughts. The Sisters of Charity, who ran the Charity Hospital, were in intimate contact with the poverty-stricken, and whenever pestilence decimated the slums and crowded wharf areas the Catholic orders, men and women, were at hand to tend the sick and give absolution to the dying. Possibly one of the best commentaries upon the efforts of all churchmen this summer was a suggestion in the *Crescent* that ministers be given free tickets for the omnibuses and railway lines to assist them in their duties. The editor noted that they were too poorly paid to be able to visit all those who needed their services.[11]

The gloom which pervaded the city on Saturday was not lightened by the events of the succeeding days. On Monday an editorial on the epidemic began by printing the Board of Health's mortality report for the week ending Saturday, August 20. A total of 1,534 burials had been officially reported, of which 1,376 had been attributed to yellow fever and another 70 were of unknown causes but were thought to have been the result of the fever. Since July 1 yellow fever had caused almost 5,000 deaths, it stated, and yet "the pestilence still rages with, if possible, augmented virulence. . . ." Formerly the "better classes" had scarcely been touched by the disorder, particularly those who had lived in the city for several years; now none were safe who had not previously had the disease, no matter how long their residence in New Orleans. As a precaution, the editor urged the authorities to prevent immigrant vessels from unloading their cargoes in New Orleans until the epidemic had subsided.[12]

As the disease intensified, men of inquiring mind desperately sought its cause. The old issue of spontaneous generation versus importation was brought up for reconsideration. The previous week a correspondent who signed himself 'H' had urged that New Orleans protect itself from future attacks by means of a quarantine. A couple of days later the editor to whom the letter was addressed, in reporting that Natchez and Baton Rouge had adopted quarantine measures with respect to New Orleans, commended their actions and suggested that it would be wise for all towns and plantations along the Mississippi River to follow suit. The next day the *Delta* picked up the story and commented that although the *Picayune* was the first of the newspapers openly to favor quarantine, it was expressing "a very prevalent sentiment." Most of the physicians, the *Delta* added, were against the idea of the transmissibility of yellow fever, but nonetheless the matter should be given a thorough study.[13]

Debatable as was the question of the communicability of yellow fever through direct contact, few individuals doubted that the foul miasma or epidemic atmosphere carried the disease particles. A significant experiment tried at this time seemed to show beyond question that the air had become corrupted. A physician attached a piece of fresh meat to a kite and flew it for twenty or thirty minutes. When the kite was returned to the ground, the meat was "completely covered with living, moving vermiform animalculae." The same results, achieved repeatedly during the epidemic, led the physician to write that these "phenomena demonstrate a horribly polluted condition of our atmosphere, and show that *that* atmosphere was permanently established around us throughout the whole epidemic." [14] Apprehensiveness about the state of the air was also shown in an article on the cemeteries which appeared about this time. The rumor that the city was burning bodies because of a lack of gravediggers had swept through New Orleans the previous weekend and was subsequently reported throughout the United States. The *Delta* explained that the rumor was started because the Board of Health had ordered immense quantities of tar to be burned in the Lafayette Cemetery "for the purpose of counteracting the pernicious influence of the corrupt air, arising from the decomposition of those bodies which were so slightly covered a week or two since." The tar had been burned at night when the cemetery was not filled with gravediggers and relatives, and it was this fact which had led people to conclude that the city was burning bodies. The flaming tar and lime spread on the graves were reported to have had their desired effect and "bad odors are no longer wafted on every breeze from this city of the dead." [15]

It was probably this same fear of putrefaction and malodorous atmosphere which impelled the sanitary inspectors to watch the markets more closely. New Orleans had had municipal ordinances against the sale of spoiled meat for a century or more, and though they were usually enforced, the inspection was never too strict. On August 22 and 23 the newspapers carried stories of arrests for infringements of these ordinances. A Mr. Fousha Gillion was caught in the act of taking the meat of a "diseased cow" to market; and John Estrade, a butcher, was charged with exposing "a putrid hog" for sale in his stall in the Magazine Street Market.[16]

On August 20, the newspapers had gloomily reported that the burials for the preceding day had reached a new high of 234. On Saturday, that same day, the death toll was 224, a slight reduction which gave some encouragement to the Board of Health; but this hope was short lived, for the next day the burials climbed to a new high. An editorial in the *Delta* entitled "The Black Day" began: "The twenty-four hours from 6 o'clock A.M. on Saturday, till 6 o'clock on Sunday, the 21st, constitute the blackest day in the gloomy annals of the fearful pestilence, which has desolated our city." No less than 269 deaths had been officially reported to the Board of Health, while another 28 bodies were said to have been buried in St. Patrick's Cemetery without certificates, and 18 more in the Hebrew graveyards. Reiterating a hope which had helped support the people as the daily total of deaths continued its remorseless climb, the editor added that he had heard from reliable sources that "the disease begins to decline, and that the worst is now over," for the physicians had all noticed a reduction in the number of cases.[17]

Whatever its editor may have felt, the other columns gave little reason for hope. One story told of the case of a businessman who, having lost his wife a few months earlier, had sent for his brother and sister. Shortly after their arrival, fever struck the household causing the death of an old servant the previous morning, the brother about noon, and now the sister was expected to die with the "black vomit." The reporter said, "We do not mention this circumstance because it is a rare one, but as an example of the destructive ravages of this dire disease." Another news item related that the epidemic had spread across the Mississippi River and was devastating the towns of Algiers and Gretna. The editor appealed for any information from these two areas since sickness and death had so reduced the reportorial corps that "we cannot find time to travel far abroad very often." [18]

Bad as the cemetery reports appeared on August 21, the next day was even worse; when the Board of Health compiled its totals from the cemeteries, the report showed 254 deaths from yellow fever and 29 more attributed to other causes. The *Bee*, like all New Orleans' papers, had almost spent itself of emotionally charged phrases by this time, and its editorial sounded strangely subdued. The confident predictions for the past several weeks that each successively higher daily death toll marked a turning point in the epidemic had proven completely wrong, and the newspaper editors scarcely knew which way to turn. Yet the very destructiveness of the epidemic meant that the peak must be close at hand. The *Bee*'s editor wrote: "Let us hope that the gloom and horror which have fallen on our city, and which, during the last forty-eight hours, have but deepened in intensity, are the precursors of brighter and more cheerful times. Surely it is well nigh impossible with our reduced population for the pestilence to rage much longer at the present fearful rate of mortality—a rate which has been gradually and daily increasing until it has reached the appalling number of Two Hundred and Fifty a day." Since 5,000 have already perished and 20,000 people have fallen sick, he concluded, surely the disease must soon subside for want of material.[19]

On August 23, the total burials dropped to 258; although New Orleans did not realize it immediately, the worst was over. In reporting the figures for that day, one journalist perceptively noted that although the reduction in mortality was only slight, it had been accompanied by "a very evident and gratifying decline in the cases admitted into the hospitals." Only thirty-one new cases had entered Charity Hospital as against forty-one the preceding day and sixty-five a week earlier. For the first time in many days the number of discharges exceeded the admissions and deaths, a fact which the editor said could "only be ascribed to the reduction or exhaustion of material." On Wednesday, August 24, the number of burials fell to 222, leading the *Crescent* to say cautiously that the fever appeared to be relaxing its grip, whether permanently or only temporarily, the editor added, remained to be seen. Up to this date, he commented with horrified amazement, out of a population of about 75,000, yellow fever had already killed 1 out of every 12½ persons.[20]

By Friday the deaths per day had fallen to 193, a drop of 90 from the preceding Monday. For the week ending Saturday, August 27, a total of 1,628 burials was reported by the Board of Health, 1,454 of which were definitely attributable to yellow fever. It was small wonder that the *Price-Current* on that day declared the city's business was "almost wholy [sic] at a stand, the fearful epidemic which has been raging for some time past, and which still continues its progress, having completely deranged all business operations." Little produce had come in from the interior, while the combination of drought in the cotton areas and sickness in the city had virtually cut off all cotton receipts.[21] By Monday, however, it was becoming evident that the crisis was past. The editor of the *Bee* seemed almost cheerful in discussing the frightening mortality of the preceding week—and with good reason. Although the first two days had witnessed the largest death toll of the outbreak, a steady reduction during the ensuing days clearly demonstrated that the epidemic wave was subsiding. The two logical explanations for this turn of events, he said, were that the pestilence had run out of material or that the fever was no longer as virulent as earlier. The medical faculty had noticed that the cases were becoming both fewer and more manageable. This fact, combined with the reduction in the death toll, inclined the editor to the belief that there had been "a modification in the virulence of the disease rather than an absence of subjects." [22]

On Saturday, August 27, the cemeteries reported 185 burials. In the ensuing days the number fell steadily; by August 31 it was down to 137; and five days later it dropped below 100 for the first time in over six weeks. Even though a feeling of relief was clearly evident in the newspapers, letters, and diaries of New Orleans, yellow fever continued throughout September to inflict what would ordinarily have been considered heavy casualties. According to the official statistics, there were 749 yellow fever deaths for the week ending September 3; 421 for the week ending September 10; 221 as of September 17; 125 as of September 24; and 85 for the week ending October 1.[23] Furthermore, these figures do not include many deaths for which no cause was given nor those which probably resulted from yellow fever but were attributed to some other disorder.

The *Delta* had unhesitatingly stated on August 22 and 23 that the peak of the outbreak had been reached, but the other journals were more cautious, having learned by bitter experience the unpredictability of yellow fever. Their attitude was best expressed by the *Bee* on August 29. After commenting upon the sharp decline in the daily burials for the past few days, the editor wrote: "So often has the press been bitterly disappointed in expressing a confident belief in the speedy disappearance of the epidemic, that even now, with the statistics before us, attesting a falling off of not less than one hundred from the greatest daily mortality of the season, we scarcely dare to do more than breathe a hope that we shall, in a few weeks, be fully rid of the pestilence." [24]

Although the tide had turned on August 22, the incredible number of daily deaths and the vast number of those still sick obscured the fact to most of the citizens. For them the rest of August and the first part of September was a continuation of the seemingly endless round of caring for the sick and burying the dead. There was no relief either for the harried Howard Association members who, in fact, found their work increasing. On August 24 one of them appealed to the public not to apply to the organization for general charity. Requests to pay back rent, provide transportation home, and care for large families were not within the realm of the Howard Association's activities, for it had been chartered solely to take care of the indigent sick during epidemics and its resources did not permit more than this. Already the association had cared for over 6,000 yellow fever cases, and it anticipated many more. Before the epidemic was over, the Howard member continued, the association expected to spend over a hundred thousand dollars on the sick, whereas half a million dollars would not suffice to handle all appeals for charity. The writer corrected the assumption that Howard members received pay; all, he said, gave their time and effort without any financial recompense.[25]

The following day an indignant physican, Dr. Edward Jenner Coxe, bitterly criticized the Howards for limiting their services, pointing out that the indirect effects of the epidemic were almost as serious as the sickness and death itself. He softened his letter by commending them for their work with the sick and dying and assured them that more money would be forthcoming. Dr. Coxe was equally unhappy about the niggardly sum appropriated by the New Orleans City Council: "Is our city so poor, are our taxes so light," he asked, "that it cannot or will not come to the rescue?" By this time thousands of dollars donated from all parts of the country had come pouring into New Orleans. Private individuals made many contributions, and the municipal authorities of nearly all large cities had sent substantial sums. Philadelphia, Coxe's original home, had been among the contributors, and he declared that he was sure Philadelphia expected its money to be used wherever necessary.[26]

Meanwhile efforts to purify the air of the city were moving ahead. In addition to providing the tar to be burned in the public squares and graveyards, the city made it available for all citizens who wished to purify their own premises. For example, on August 23 a brief letter to the newspapers from Captain Baldwin of the police force read: "Gents— you will please notify the public that there will be tar at the Police office opposite Jackson Square, for distribution to-morrow." Alas, these efforts proved of little value according to the *Delta*, for few individuals took advantage of the offer. This same journal complained on August 25 that not enough tar was being burned and that the small quantity which was burned was not distributed properly. The *Delta* suggested that a barrel or half-barrel should be burned at every intersection in the infected districts, instead of, "as is the case now, a little scattered along Canal street, and a few barrels dispersed at wide distances through the city." The *Delta*'s complaint about the inadequate quantity of burning tar was purely relative, since the article concluded by saying that a stranger approaching the city at nightfall "would suppose from the dense volumes of black smoke arising from the various points, caused by the burning tar, that we carried on a manufacturing business equal to that of Manchester, Pittsburgh, or Wheeling. So we do," he added, "but it is of a more grave character." [27]

During the next few days, several other suggestions were made to help remove the poisoned air, or "epidemic constitution." A letter signed "Medicus," from one who described himself as an old practitioner in Mobile, recommended pouring oil of vitriol on common salt. Fires, he wrote, should be kept burning day and night, and it would help if handfuls of green coffee were thrown on the fires at intervals for coffee fumes were a powerful disinfectant. One New Orleans editor cited the case of Charleston, South Carolina, where the city authorities had made ample provision for cleaning the streets and drying all cellars flooded by rains. Had the New Orleans officials concentrated upon keeping the city clean rather than arguing over the duties of the street commissioner, he declared, the epidemic might not have started. As an incidental suggestion, the editor passed on the recommendation of "a scientific friend" that all houses be fumigated with pure chlorine and gave specific directions for so doing.[28]

With what may have been only slightly tongue in cheek, the *Weekly Delta* recommended on August 28 that the city hire a band to parade through the streets rather than spending money to burn tar and gunpowder. "The genial strains," declared the paper, "will tend to elevate the minds and raise spirits" far more than "the firing of all the cannon in the arsenal." Reflecting the rising spirit of optimism on August 31, another journal facetiously discussed a proposal to parch coffee as a means of purifying the air. Noting that the high price of coffee would cause the city to run heavily into debt if it should try this method, it proposed as a more feasible expedient to parch the coffee brokers and dealers. The story was undoubtedly a sly dig at the high cost of coffee, but it indicates that the fear and tension engendered by the epidemic were abating.[29]

In a more serious vein, the *Delta* discussed the problem of the New Orleans graveyards where the dead were buried only a few inches below the surface and urged that consideration be given to cremation, a much more sanitary method for taking care of the dead. The paper noted that a Mississippi physician had suggested that the city carry the bodies down the Mississippi and bury them at sea, but it felt this was impractical. From Donaldsonville, Louisiana, Dr. Fred B. Page wrote advising interns in the hospitals to use the same precautionary measures which had helped an eminent physician of the marine barracks at Brest to escape "several putrid and pestilential diseases." Before visiting the hospitals, the physician inserted a small sponge moistened with essential oil into his nostrils and kept a piece of orange peel in his mouth. Dr. Page's advice to the citizens in general was that they could avoid the disease (this suggestion was a little belated in view of the number already dead!) by clean living, temperance, the avoidance of undue exposure, and the regular use of a pill consisting of 1½ grains of quinine, ½ grain of pepper extract, and ¼ grain of extract of belladona.[30] The only way Dr. Page's precautions could have prevented yellow fever would have been to feed his pill to the *Aedes aegypti*, the yellow fever mosquito, but in retrospect this scarcely seems practical.

Toward the end of August the much-debated subject of quarantine measures was once again in the newspapers. One correspondent argued the case for the transmissibility of yellow fever, pointing to instances during previous epidemics which suggested that the disease was clearly imported. The following day another newspaper considered the question in its editorial columns. "The effort has been repeatedly made," declared its editor, "to settle this vexed question by physicians of profound sagacity, immense experience, and almost unlimited opportunity for observation," yet the debate still continues. As a newspaperman, he was in no position to pass judgment on so serious a medical issue, the editor wrote, yet he felt constrained to admit that the "weight of authority is overwhelming in favor of the local origin of Yellow Fever." [31]

The *Bee's* support for those who argued that the disease was spontaneously generated in New Orleans led the *Picayune* in its next issue to declare itself firmly in favor of a quarantine law. With medical and scientific men divided on the issue, the *Picayune* was willing to concede the validity of arguments in favor of sanitary measures and agree that cleanliness and a pure atmosphere might well contribute to preventing the disease. However, since the matter was still undecided, it seemed far wiser to pursue both policies and add quarantine measures to the existing sanitary laws. Over and above the possibility of preventing the introduction of disease into the city, a quarantine law would stop immigrants from landing, thereby saving lives and reducing the intensity of the epidemic.[32]

The immigrant problem had been taken up a day or two earlier by the *Louisiana Courier* which demanded that the Board of Health exclude "fresh subjects for the yellow fever" from New Orleans. The editor declared that on the previous Sunday, August 28, forty-three passengers had landed from Le Havre. He had been horrified to find some of them walking on the sunny side of the street and had warned them of the danger, but they had paid no heed to his advice. In discussing the need to prevent the arrival of unacclimated newcomers, the editor asserted that although we "are told by some wiseacres that the epidemic is abating . . . this is no proof that the virulence of the disease has in the slightest degree subsided, or that the atmosphere is purer." The Board of Health had actually anticipated the problem two days earlier, for on August 26 it had resolved to organize a quarantine commission to deal with ships and passengers entering the port. The *Bee* applauded this action in an editorial headed, "An Excellent Movement," which concluded by stating: "It is indisputable that the presence of a fresh batch of unacclimated persons, while the fever is still raging, will maintain it in full virulence." [33]

With the city leaders and newspapers exploring all avenues in search of relief, it was not to be wondered that the thoughts of many citizens turned to religion, both as a source of solace and as a means for stopping the frightful pestilence. On August 12 a notice signed by three Methodist ministers appeared in the newspapers stating that those needing a clergyman to visit the sick or bury the dead could contact the three men by writing instructions "on the slate at 36 Camp street (office of the Christian Advocate)" between the hours of 8 A.M. and 2 P.M. The names and addresses of the ministers were appended, and the notice added that at any other hours, the clergymen should be contacted at their homes.[34] As the epidemic intensified and all counter measures proved useless, the clergy, following a long tradition, appealed for public prayer. The association of sickness and pestilence with the supernatural is one of the oldest beliefs in society, and the Christian world was no exception. Epidemics were invariably attributed to the wrath of God, and it had long been the custom to proclaim days of fasting and prayer whenever epidemic disease struck down the godly and ungodly alike. Despite wide advances in all fields of science and a tremendous accumulation of medical knowledge, epidemic disorders remained almost as much of a mystery as they had been in early Christian times. Mankind, as theologians had preached for centuries, was tainted with original sin, and it was hard even for the most virtuous to stay on the narrow and slippery path of rectitude. Sinfulness was rampant, according to the preachers, and the ever-growing worldliness was certain to bring down the wrath of Divine Providence. Only three years earlier President Zachary Taylor had proclaimed a national day of fasting, prayer, and humiliation in the face of a nationwide Asiatic cholera outbreak, and for New Orleanians the yellow fever threat was an even greater crisis.

On August 24 the newspapers carried appeals by a number of clergy-men. Four Presbyterian ministers called for a "Union Meeting" for humiliation and prayer every afternoon at 5 P.M. in the Second Presby-terian Church on the corner of Prytania and Calliope streets. Bishop Polk of the Protestant Episcopal Church, who had seen yellow fever strike down many of his flock, had already prepared a special prayer to be used by all churches in his diocese during the epidemic; on this same day, the Reverend Dr. Leacock of Christ's Church declared the coming Friday, August 26, to be a "day of humiliation, [and] of prayer to the Most High for his relief and protection of Our City, over which the Destroying Angel holds sway." [35]

The prayer issued by Bishop Polk read:

Oh! Almighty and merciful God, to whom alone belong the issues of life and death, we, thy servants, bowed down under a deep sense of our unworthi-ness, do meekly acknowledge that we have grievously sinned, by thought, word and deed against thy Divine Majesty; and that by our sins we have most justly provoked thy wrath and indignation against us. But oh! God, who desireth not the death of a sinner but rather that he should turn from his wickedness and live, be merciful unto us, be merciful unto thy people who turn to Thee with unfeigned confession and humiliation, and give us grace, that we may truly repent us of our sins past, and be turned unto Thee, the Lord our God, with full purpose of amendment of life. Spare us, good Lord, spare thy servants, who are grieved with the remembrance of our sins, and turn from us the ravages of the pestilence, wherewith, for our iniquities Thou art now visiting us. And mercifully grant that while this, thy Fatherly cor-rection, may teach us, ever, hereafter, to be mindful of Thy righteous judg-ment, it may also impress us, with a sense of our dependence upon Thee; lead us, now, to put our whole trust and confidence in Thy mercy, and ever-more to serve and please Thee, in newness of life, through Jesus Christ our Lord. *Amen.*

The announcement by the four Presbyterian ministers which began "As God's hand is now heavy upon us . . ." emphasized the same points made in Bishop Polk's prayer. All Christians were urged to humble themselves before God, to supplicate "Him to deliver us from the pesti-lence that now desolates our city," and to pray that He might "be pleased to turn his anger away from us, . . . and incline the hearts of all men to learn righteousness when His judgments are abroad in the land." [36]

With the churches holding special services, it was to be expected that the city officials would soon fall into line. On August 30 Mayor Cross-man officially proclaimed the following Friday, September 2, to be a day of prayer and humiliation. His proclamation, which began: "Whereas, It has pleased the Supreme Being, in the dispensations of an All-wise, but

inscrutable Providence to lay the heavy hand of Pestilence on our devoted city," stated that although Christians should bear their afflictions
"with calm fortitude and resignation," it was also proper for them "to
petition Him in his mercy to spare us the last drop of bitterness, and
thereby make us more sensible of his Goodness and Omnipotence." All
citizens, "without distinction of sect, nation or age," were requested to
"refrain from their usual avocations of business, close their stores, offices,
shops and public places in order that . . . we may all observe the said day
as one set especially apart for solemn thought [and] religious exercise. . . ." [37]

On September 2 the daily papers urged all citizens to participate in
the religious observances. The churches opened their doors for special
services at 11 o'clock, and even the post office closed at this hour. If the
disastrous events of the preceding two months had not served to turn the
minds of the New Orleanians toward spiritual things, the clomping of
horses' hooves and the rumbling of hearses through the streets were grim
reminders that the pestilence still walked among them. There was little
inclination toward careless gaiety in New Orleans on this solemn day,
and its citizens turned to their churches in an unprecedented fashion.
Never before, declared one of the newspapers, had the city witnessed
such "a general closing up of places of business. . . ." All public offices,
courts, hotels, and coffeehouses shut their doors, while the "church bells,
from every part of the city, pealed forth an earnest invitation for our
people to assemble in the sanctuaries of the Most High, and offer up their
supplications and prayers to Him. Nor did the bells call in vain," the
paper added, "for thousands of our people responded and thronged the
various places of worship." [38]

As the city lifted its voice in supplication, asking God to spare New
Orleans from His wrath, only the indomitable Dr. Clapp spoke in opposition. He had long ago recanted the faith of his youth, that of a fierce
Old Testament Jehovah who held His people in subjection through fear.
His was a God of Love, and Parson Clapp could no more conceive of the
idea of God inflicting pestilence and death upon the just and unjust alike
than he could accept the equally gloomy concepts of predestination and
infant damnation. In a statement issued to the Picayune on September
2 he asked whether the people of New Orleans were any more deserving
of Heaven's wrath than those of London, Paris, Boston, or New York.
Was God particularly angry, he asked, with the faithful clergyman who
only a few days earlier had died from the fever in the performance of
his duties? He could not believe that God was either vindictive or capa-

ble of infinite vengeance, and he was sure that God's love was as present on this day of fasting and humiliation in New Orleans as it had ever been.[39] These heretical views would certainly have brought down the wrath of New Orleans upon the head of a lesser man, but for thirty years Dr. Clapp's life had exemplified the Christian ethic and demonstrated the validity of Christian brotherhood. No one who knew him—and he was the most prominent churchman in New Orleans in his day—could question that here was a man who had sought faithfully to follow the Christian way of life. The orthodox might shake their heads but Dr. Clapp's position was virtually impregnable. Moreover, crossing verbal swords over theological questions with Dr. Clapp, even in his declining years, was no task to be lightly undertaken.

Throughout the outbreak the newspapers continued to publish their daily editions despite what must have been severe difficulties. Only occasionally did their columns indicate any of the problems which beset them during the long weeks when sickness and death reduced their staffs to an absolute minimum. On August 16, the *Delta*, which suffered particularly heavy casualties, apologized for the appearance of the Sunday paper, explaining that the editorial and composing room staff had been sadly reduced by the prevailing sickness. A few days later the paper mentioned that half of the compositors were sick, that two had already died, and that the staff were now compelled to add "another victim to the ghostly records of death's doings in our midst." The latest victim was a newly employed reporter, Mr. Frederick Gibson, a young Irishman who had only recently lost his sister and her child to the yellow fever.[40] Three days later the *Delta* reported the death of the foreman of the press room, Mr. Charles H. Brady. An even greater loss occurred on August 30. Dr. William K. Northall, one of the editors, feeling near the end of August that the worst was over, decided to go to New York to arrange for the return of his children. Although he was unaware of it, yellow fever had already laid its deadly grip upon him, and death came to him a scant day's journey from New Orleans. On September 4 the paper lost its seventh man, a young printer from Virginia; all of the victims, it was noted gloomily, had died within the space of three weeks![41]

Even at the peak of the outbreak the newspapers maintained an incredibly calm and objective approach to local news. Mayor Crossman and those officials who remained at their posts were doing their utmost to ease the crisis, and the newspapers refrained from excessive criticism, though they made no attempt to gloss over conditions. Under the head-

This sketch depicts two children returning home with coffins for other members of their family. New Orleans newspapers carried appeals on behalf of the many children orphaned by the epidemic.

ing of "Local Affairs," for example, the *Delta* reported the case of an old lady who had requested the authorities to bury her husband. Shortly thereafter one of the city wagons appeared bearing a wood coffin. Since the body was on the second floor and the Negro driver had no one to help him put the coffin in the cart, the sorrowing widow had been compelled to help carry it downstairs. Bowed down by years and weakened by grief, the added strain had caused her collapse. In calling attention to this instance, the journal mildly suggested that henceforth an assistant accompany the drivers. A day later another paper complained about the crowds of rowdies who were disturbing the sick and wanted to know what the police were doing to permit such things to happen.[42]

Even though it was quick to draw public attention to abuses, injustices, and negligence, the *Delta* was also willing to give credit where it was due. On August 18, an editorial commended the public officials for their benevolence and zeal, praised the work of the many charitable organizations, and added with pride that "we feel, indeed, that New Orleans may justly claim a pre-eminence in the philanthropy and noble courage of her people." Apropos the latter statement, one of its reporters had visited several of the poorer class and was both pleased and surprised to note the prudence and discretion with which they treated the disease "and the attention and devotion to their sick friends." [43] In view of the almost universal assumption by the middle and upper classes that the poor brought on disease by their dissolute, immoral, and intemperate lives, one can only assume that the yellow fever had had a sobering effect upon the poor or else had made the upper classes more tolerant!

Probably a good illustration of the casual manner in which the residents of New Orleans accepted the harsh blows of destiny was their reaction to an announcement on August 24 that because of the prevailing fever, the public schools would not open until the first Monday in October. An outraged letter, signed "A Teacher," appeared in one of the papers bitterly criticizing the school boards for their decision. Some of the poor mothers had burst into tears, the letter asserted, upon hearing the news. When the writer had been hired in 1847, the first question she had been asked was whether or not she intended to remain in the city during the summers. Those applicants who answered in the negative had not been hired; hence the writer felt that all teachers should be acclimated and available for school work as usual.[44] The school boards, however, remained unconvinced, and the decision was allowed to stand.

In the state of Louisiana, politics has traditionally been a favorite pastime, and the state's history is replete with colorful figures and events.

Epidemic or no epidemic, politics as usual was the order of the day, and the editorial columns devoted far more space to discussing local and national politics while the yellow fever was making its terrible attack than was given to the epidemic. Although most of the editorials were sober political discussions reflecting the party affiliation or inclination of the various journals, on at least one occasion several newspapers speculated upon the effect of the epidemic upon the coming election. The *Orleanian* sought to irritate one of the Democratic journals by suggesting that the high death rate among the poorer classes would greatly reduce the strength of the Democratic party. The editor of the *Daily Crescent*, who took note of the exchange, was shocked to think that in the midst of an epidemic men "should cooly reason, . . . on the probable good or bad fortune to befall a political party in consequence of a terrible mortality. . . ." Nonetheless, he felt compelled to admit that four-fifths of those who had escaped the fever by fleeing the city were Whigs, while the poor and unacclimated class which bore the brunt of the disease belonged largely to the Democratic party. He would have hesitated to mention the subject himself, the editor wrote, but since others were voicing it, he had to conclude that "when Whigs from the North return in November, they will carry the elections their own way." [45]

The attitude of the newspapers demonstrates one of the great lessons to be learned from studying early epidemics—the incredible elasticity and resiliency of human life. New Orleans had witnessed ghastly scenes in its cemeteries, had seen thousands of its inhabitants carried away by a horrible disease within the space of a few weeks, had watched trade and commerce grind to a halt, and yet, almost as soon as the peak of the epidemic was passed, one senses a quickening and a revival. On August 25 and 26 two of the newspapers spoke in glowing terms of the prosperity and growth of the city: there had never been a time when so many new buildings were in process; the introduction of the omnibuses had caused the suburbs to blossom; old buildings were coming down to make room for the new; and on the edges of the city new homes were appearing as rapidly as the swamps and lagoons were filled in. And all of this, the *Daily Crescent* added, despite a scarcity of "hands" and a "consequent rise in the price of labor." [46]

As September dawned, yellow fever deaths were still running in excess of one hundred per day, but the steady and rapid decline in the daily mortality from the high point reached on August 22 and the equally sharp reduction in the number of new cases clearly showed that the worst was over. The harried doctors and nurses, Howard Association members, and all others working with the sick still had much to do, but the sense of urgency and apprehension was gone. Intimate contact with yellow fever victims for so many weeks had given all a sense of familiarity with the scourge, thereby removing at least part of its terror. Hospital facilities were no longer so crowded, and the smoothly operating administrative organizations established by the civic authorities and the many private organizations were easily able to cope with the new cases of yellow fever. Even as its citizens prepared themselves for the day of fasting and prayer on September 2, the reader of the newspapers is conscious of a great feeling of relief, a quickening of hope, and a revival of the buoyant optimism that had characterized New Orleans for so many years.

CHAPTER VII

Passing of the Plague

THE FEELING OF RELIEF which swept through New Orleans with the advent of September was born of knowledge that the crisis was past, but by no means did it signify immediate relief from the ever-present threat of sickness and death. The September issue of the *New Orleans Medical & Surgical Journal* appeared on schedule bearing a short editorial by Dr. Hester. He apologized for any shortcomings in the *Journal.* "Our attention," he wrote, "has been given for the most part, to those stricken down by the epidemic during the last six weeks; and we have had neither the time nor that calmness of spirit which would enable us to collect and arrange our thoughts for publication." His energies, he continued, had been "taxed to the utmost of their power and endurance," and for hours and hours "sleep, so necessary to our well-being, has long been denied us." During the few available moments of leisure, he had found that "the mind was too weary and the heart too sad to perform our editorial duties." [1]

This same sadness of spirit was reflected in the *Bee* on September 1. A front page poem entitled, *The Fevered City,* by the Reverend Charles W. Denison, somberly pictured the judgment which had fallen upon New Orleans. While this little work gives the Reverend Denison no claim to poetic immortality, he used the ornate rhetoric of his day with telling effect, and the second verse graphically depicts the horrors just witnessed by the people of New Orleans:

> Oh! ye who breath amid no fevered air,
> Think of the woes your southern kinsmen bear!
> Oh ye who sport along Atlantic's shore,
> Think of that perished host ye meet no more!

Call up those silent streets—that lone levee—
And the unburied dead swept to the sea!
Go to that funeral pyre, whose flames arise
To light with horrid glare the midnight skies!
Stand where the putrid heaps begrime the sod,
Whose trembling souls, unshriven have gone to God!
Toil with the HOWARD's mid the crowded room
Where dying shrieks and groans pierce through the gloom!
But seek ye not the dead; seek those who live,
And of your substance, quick! oh! quickly, give![2]

In sharp contrast to the grim pictures painted by Dr. Hester and the Reverend Denison, the newspapers generally looked optimistically to the future. On September 2 the *Picayune* reported that although yellow fever deaths were still running about one hundred per day, there could be little doubt that the disease was on the wane. Filled with an even more cheerful spirit, the *Price-Current* did not even deign to notice the epidemic. In an editorial on September 1 summarizing the commercial activity for the preceding year, the journal congratulated the community "upon the enjoyment of a season of general prosperity." The planters could rejoice in "ample crops and remunerating prices" while the merchants could "have reason to be satisfied with the season's operations." Not only had the past year been highly successful, but the "indications would seem to be auspicious for the season now entered upon." Good crops, high prices, and "the noble works of internal improvement now in progress" should enable the city to move forward even more rapidly than it had in the past.[3] As a commercial newspaper, the *Price-Current* may be forgiven for dwelling on economic matters, but one cannot help wondering whether it really was representative of the views of the merchants and businessmen of New Orleans. Even those who had suffered no losses in their immediate families must have been appalled at the manner in which the pestilence had devastated their associates and employees. Whatever their economic gains, businessmen could scarcely have derived much satisfaction from glancing back over the previous season.

On this same day the editor of the *Delta* was in an equally confident mood. In an almost cheerful editorial on the condition of the cemeteries, he described the graveyards as being in excellent shape, but the implications in his editorial belied his complacent views. The editor had visited all graveyards and found them to be in good order. Although the roads leading to them were jammed with hearses, carriages, and people on foot awaiting their turn to be admitted, the crowds were quiet and orderly. At Cypress Grove No. 2, one of the main cemeteries, an ample supply of gravediggers and laborers was available. For many weeks forty to fifty dead had been buried there daily, the editor continued; but despite these large numbers, the graves were being dug three to four feet in depth, and the laborers were rapidly clearing and preparing new burial grounds. Despite the lack of religious ceremonies for burials of the poor, the friends and relatives who clustered around the graves showed appropriate respect, and the "half-naked negroes, who superintend the burials, observed a proper solemnity and performed their disagreeable duties in a proper manner." [4]

St. Patrick's Cemetery, which had been the subject of considerable criticism, was found to be in equally satisfactory condition. Only a few days earlier the Board of Health had resolved to send a notice to the pastor of St. Patrick's Church drawing his attention to the shameful neglect on the part of the sexton. The priest was requested to replace this caretaker, to secure enough laborers to bury the dead without delay, and to make daily returns of all burials to the Board of Health. For this purpose, the board had prepared a form showing the name, age, occupation, disease, nativity, and other particulars with respect to the deceased. The sexton of St. Patrick's had been reporting the number of burials but had refused to fill out individual burial certificates. The detailed form was designed to provide information for friends and relatives from out of the city. Moreover, it was the intention of the Board of Health at the end of the epidemic to publish a complete list of all victims and their respective places of burial. On August 29 the board had instructed the city attorney to file charges against the sexton. Apparently the threat of action proved sufficient, since the *Delta* specifically mentioned on September 1 that the situation at St. Patrick's had been corrected.[5]

In defending the cemetery, the *Delta* gave a good clue to part of the trouble. The current stories about St. Patrick's had been exaggerated, the editor said, for most of the problems had been caused by the too free use of ardent spirits and by the efforts of individual groups to obtain particular burial spots. Complaints had been voiced earlier about burial parties breaking down the cemetery fences in order to bypass waiting lines or to conduct burials at night, and about occasional fights breaking out between some of the groups over the use of burial plots. All parties concerned, the editor happily reported, had been rebuked, and the cemetery was now in good order. He noted further that "the noxious effluvia" came largely from those cemeteries where people could afford to be interred above ground in costly tombs; the cemeteries for the poor, where the coffins were buried in the ground, remained quite free of all offensive odors.[6]

Surprising as it may seem, a few immigrant vessels from Europe continued to arrive in New Orleans throughout the epidemic, and it was not until the latter part of August that the city fathers became seriously concerned. Late in the month the Board of Health established a Committee on Quarantine and Emigrants with Mr. Kursheedt in charge. After some prodding by the newspapers, the committee formally requested permission from the United States government to use Fort St. Philip, some sixty miles down the Mississippi River, and Fort Jackson as quarantine stations. Meanwhile the committee assumed charge of inspecting incoming vessels. On August 29, for example, a ship from Le Havre arrived with forty passengers. Representatives of the committee visited the vessel, found the passengers and crew healthy, and made arrangements to send them on to their destinations. Establishing quarantine measures in the midst of a major epidemic seems paradoxical, but the Board of Health really was concerned with preventing the landing of what they termed "new subjects" for yellow fever. When Mr. Kursheedt reported on September 1 that no word had been received from Washington with respect to Fort St. Philip and Fort Jackson, the board decided in the event of further delay to establish its own quarantine stations. Indicating its concern with keeping the number of nonimmunes to a minimum, the board requested Mayor Crossman to notify civic authorities in all river towns to warn the unacclimated to stay away from New Orleans.[7]

Three days later the United States Army offered the use of both Fort Jackson and Fort St. Philip. Fort Jackson was designated as the main receiving station, and arrangements were made promptly to fit it up for the reception of immigrants. On September 8 a letter was received from the superintendent of Fort Jackson stating that he was prepared to receive five hundred immigrants and would be able to accommodate one thousand within a few days. This same day the mayor and the Board of Health officially ordered all passengers ascending the Mississippi River to be landed at the quarantine grounds at Fort Jackson. The *Picayune* cheerfully remarked at this time that for want of subjects the fever seemed to be rapidly abating, and with the Board of Health authorized to prevent "new fuel" from coming into the city, it felt that the disease should soon disappear. The newspaper closed with a strong warning to all outsiders to keep out of the city until after the first frost.[8]

A revealing article in one of the daily journals on September 4 stated that the disease was virtually gone from the First and Fourth districts but was still systematically working through the streets and sections of the lower portions of the city. The Second District, the story related, appeared to be hardest hit, judging by the hearses, the doctor's gigs, the bits of crepe fastened to doors and windows, and the many notices of business closures. In the uptown sections, however, "the drug stores are not thronged as they were wont to be a week ago," and the apothecaries now await the chance customer. The quietness in the uptown section where the pestilence had run its course, the story said, was almost the quietness of death. Upon asking an old lady about the state of her neighborhood, she had replied: "Oh, sirs, its very healthy here now." "Healthy!" said we, in surprise. "Yes, sir," said she! "They be all dead—indeed, there be not fifteen left in the whole street." [9]

Almost daily during the epidemic, newspapers had reported gifts of money from individuals, from groups, and from city governments throughout the country. As it became evident that the intensity of the onslaught was lessening, The Bee, on September 5, cited the Board of Health figures of 814 deaths from yellow fever in the preceding week and expressed the hope that donations would continue. Over and above the needs of the thousands still sick, additional funds were required for widows and orphans. The total of 814 deaths attributed to yellow fever, or almost 120 per day, makes a startling contrast with the relieved and hopeful tone of the newspaper editorials. Yet all things are relative, and the number of cases and deaths was rapidly diminishing. The bleak past and the grim present were only made bearable by the thought of brighter prospects for the future. Clearly the people of New Orleans were demonstrating the irrepressibility of the human spirit.[10]

Almost as if to compensate for their refusal to face up to the presence of yellow fever in June and early July, the New Orleans papers in September tempered their confident observations on the decline of the epidemic with warnings to unacclimated strangers to stay out of the city. Even the acclimated, the Crescent wrote on September 6, are not exempt from the prevailing scourge. Among the victims were many natives and other residents who had formerly contracted yellow fever "and who have received certificates to that effect from learned physicians, in the shape of full-sized bills for medical attendance." A day later the *Delta*, in warning against over-confidence, emphasized the need for precautions to avoid another disaster the following summer. "Twice 7,000 immigrants and unacclimated persons" would enter the city in the coming year, it proclaimed, thus providing ample material for a new epidemic, which, like the present one, might affect old and new residents alike. Moreover, reports were abroad that New Orleans had been depopulated by the epidemic and that there was a desperate shortage of clerks. Most of the losses, said the editor, had been suffered by the laboring classes, and there were hundreds of clerks already looking for jobs; hence both laborers and clerks were advised to keep away from the city.[11]

Throughout September the newspapers continued to harp on this theme. One of them declared on September 11 that "the virus still lurks in our midst" and needs only the importation of unacclimated strangers to double the present mortality rate. Even the acclimated were urged to remain away, while the unacclimated were warned that it was extremely dangerous to come to New Orleans. "Unless compelled to do so by an absolute necessity, admitting of no denial," the newspaper stated, "they are best where they are—anywhere but here." On September 12 the Board of Health got into the picture by resolving that it was "highly dangerous for strangers to visit our city" and asking the authorities and newspapers in all river towns and cities to advise people to stay away from New Orleans. The resolution was formally published in the city newspapers, on the assumption that it would be picked up and reprinted far and wide.[12]

Interspersed with the warnings to outsiders, small news items showed how deeply the epidemic had affected the city. On September 6 the *Crescent* mentioned: "Some of our printers crawled out from their sick rooms yesterday morning, looking the very picture of hatchet-faced wretchedness." A day later the *Delta* praised Workhouse Superintendent J. Worrell and his assistant. Under the direction of these two men, the inmates of the Workhouse had produced sixteen hundred coffins during the summer months. This figure represented only a fraction of the coffins used to bury the approximately eleven thousand persons who died in New Orleans this terrible summer.

At the end of the second week in September the Board of Health surveyed the temporary infirmaries and was delighted to discover that the number of patients had declined sharply. Infirmary No. 1 held only one female patient, while the other three infirmaries held twenty-two, thirty-three, and thirty-one patients respectively. Consequently the board ordered that all new yellow fever cases be sent to Charity Hospital and that the infirmaries be closed as soon as the last patients were discharged. As a safety precaution, the board further decreed that all old clothing and bedding from the infirmaries should be burned under the supervision of the superintendents. A common belief about yellow fever was that it could be transmitted by "fomites" or particles of infection attached to or imbedded in clothing or linens. This fear occasionally led to an accusation that New Orleans permitted clothing and linens from yellow fever victims to be sold as rags. While this may have happened in individual cases dying in boarding houses or private homes, the municipal authorities were always very zealous in burning these articles and in fumigating with sulphur smoke the rooms of the sick. As an additional indication of the brightening outlook, the board further resolved to pay off the health wardens on September 15. These latter had been hired late in July to inspect the sanitary conditions of the various sections of the city.[13]

The tendency for yellow fever patients who survived the crisis to die suddenly during convalescence from hemorrhage or some other factor had long been recognized. Hence, although the city closed its temporary infirmaries, the Howard Association kept open the Convalescent Asylum located in the Masonic Hall. The directors, Mr. Henry Bier and P. Conniff, proudly reported on September 16 that not one patient had relapsed, a record all the more remarkable in view of the number under care.[14]

For the remainder of September the newspapers continued to publish daily and weekly bills of mortality and to write occasional editorials commenting upon the total deaths to date. Almost every one of these editorials warned strangers and the unacclimated to keep away until the first frost. On September 19, it was reported that 365 deaths had occurred during the week ending September 17, of which 243 resulted from yellow fever. While noting that the yellow fever deaths had decreased since the previous week by 217, a journalist commented that it was still "unsafe to predict the disappearance of the disease. . . ." A week later the yellow fever deaths had fallen to 153, a fact which was attributed to the "exceedingly cool" weather during which the temperature had not reached 80 degrees even at midday. On this same day, September 26, the *Crescent* editorialized upon the cumulative toll of 10,739 deaths since May 28. The editor noted that the number of deaths during the past four months had almost reached "the astonishing figure of 11,000. This," he continued, "out of a population which has been estimated at 75,000, is largely over a decimation, and shows a picture of destruction frightful to contemplate." [15]

The bills of mortality listed thirty-four burials for September 26, only twelve of which resulted from yellow fever. In setting forth these figures, the Board of Health announced that since the fever was no longer epidemic, no more daily cemetery returns would be issued. The *Delta* considered the step premature, but consoled itself with the thought that the small number of daily deaths and the immense crowds in the streets "would seem to warrant the belief that the air of our city is no longer infected with the germs of the pestilence." Enough doubts were expressed to cause the board to reconsider its action, and the daily returns were issued for another week. On October 4, however, it was announced that since some of the cemeteries were no longer submitting their daily reports, the Board of Health, feeling that the epidemic had run its course, would henceforth compile only weekly mortality reports. An equally significant indication of the decline of yellow fever at this time was an advertisement by one of the druggists stating that he was reducing the prices of his "preservatives against yellow fever." [16]

The end of September found the New Orleans newspapers once again defending the city's honor. The Baltimore *Patriot* had described the New Orleans papers as being "intimidated by their terrible condition into a forced composure of calculation. . . . While the destroyer hovers above them," it asserted, "their sole resort for consolation is the census table, distinguishing between those who have already passed through the plague ordeal, and those who . . . are not shielded by acclimation against the stroke of Death." Somewhat bitterly, the editor of the *Delta* asked what the newspapers should have done—fly from their posts "as they would do, no doubt, at the North . . . ?" In reply to an additional charge that acclimated New Orleanians were callous toward the suffering of strangers, the editorial, pointing to the effective way in which the city had organized for relief purposes, concluded that New Orleans should be admired rather than besmirched.[17]

On the same day the *Picayune* turned its editorial guns upon the English press which it said had presented a distorted picture of the epidemic plus a "full indictment for all our imagined shortcomings, natural, social, and political. . . ." It was to be expected that the English press would use the pestilence as an occasion for a homily upon slavery, but, said the *Picayune* editor, the English newspapers now "find the ordinary sanitary, physical and moral condition of New Orleans to be horrid." A third newspaper, the *Crescent*, was more concerned with confounding northern critics. Despite the efforts of the northern press to smother the truth about the prevalence of disease in the North, the *Crescent* wrote, it had incontrovertible evidence that yellow fever was raging "to a most appalling degree" in certain northern localities. In Philadelphia, where, according to its editorial writer, both the Board of Health and the doctors were trying to hide the facts, yellow fever was reported to be the talk of the town. As proof of its charge, the paper cited a letter from a "reliable gentleman" in Philadelphia who knew of four deaths from yellow fever in his washerwoman's household. The *Bee* contented itself with praising the spirit of the people of New Orleans during the past calamitous time. There had never been any evidence of panic, and it "was something marvellous to observe the stern endurance, the settled constancy, the cool and resolute, and unfaltering spirit with which our citizens battled with the death fiend." [18]

Throughout September business remained very slack. As news of the epidemic had gradually spread abroad, the number of incoming vessels had dropped. Moreover, by late August yellow fever had begun to appear widely along the Gulf Coast and in the many river and bayou towns along Louisiana's numerous waterways. These local epidemics further disrupted trade by adding to the number of areas quarantined. It soon became almost impossible to travel, for every town unaffected by the disease sought to isolate itself from all infected areas. On October 1 the *Price-Current* explained that the failure of business to take its normal upturn was due to yellow fever, as "its great malignancy and long continuance [had] in a measure deranged the whole machinery of our commerce. . . ." [19]

The advent of October brought a quickening of the city's life. The *Bee* declared on October 3 that the fever would probably not disappear until the first frost, but that it appeared the "pestilential germ" was dying from exhaustion. Otherwise, how could one explain the rapidly diminishing number of cases "in spite of the imprudent arrival amongst us of large numbers of unacclimated persons." Three days later the *Crescent* reported that the weather was clear and delightful, that yellow fever had entirely disappeared, thus making the city one of the most healthful in the country, and that people were flocking in by the thousands. "Mechanics, laborers, professionals, thieves, gamblers, vagabonds and cut-throats, all animated with the prospect of finding everybody dead, and no competition to interfere with them in making an honest living, are beginning to crowd upon us," continued its reporter with tongue in cheek, "and things look like the revival of the good old times. We think the absentees may as well come home." [20]

By Saturday, October 8, a general "re-opening of business" was noted; it was announced that several firms which had closed their doors early during the epidemic were now preparing to resume normal business hours. An even more heartening sign was the opening of the social season. Friday, October 7, witnessed a trotting match in the afternoon and a concert for the benefit of the Female Asylum in the evening. Both affairs were well attended, and the ladies, "who no longer fear the night air, graced the concert in great numbers." Two theaters, the New Hippodrome of Dan Rice and the Old St. Charles, were preparing to open their doors, and one newspaper urged the owners to hurry for the city was sadly in need of amusement.

As if to emphasize the truth of this last statement Dr. Samuel Choppin, house surgeon of Charity Hospital, issued a report covering the period from May 27 to October 3. In slightly over four months, the hospital had admitted 2,960 cases of yellow fever. Of these, 1,600 had died. In explanation of the 54 percent case fatality rate, Dr. Choppin pointed out that 168 patients had been dead on admittance and many others had been beyond medical help at the time of admission. A rather poignant note which recurs in the newspapers at this time was the repeated appeals on behalf of the many orphaned children. In October the city orphanages were filled to overflowing; the Howard Association had 139 children under its care, and the Board of Health was providing for almost as many more. As the Howard Association began to reduce its work in New Orleans, the children were distributed among the permanent orphanages, with the association contributing $100 toward each child's upkeep. A series of benefit concerts, fireworks displays, and other fundraising events were held during the fall. For example, the Philadelphia Society of the Friends of Art presented a concert on Lafayette Square on October 20 and collected $222.15 for St. Mary's Catholic Boys' Asylum. On October 25 a "pyrotechnical display" was held in the square for the benefit of the Female Orphan Asylum. The announcement for this latter event mentioned that over 300 children were housed in the Female Orphan Asylum and that a great many more were expected in a few days.[21]

As the month drew on, New Orleans rapidly began returning to normality. On Monday, October 10, the public schools opened, and most of them were well attended. In the First District many of the

One of the wards at Charity Hospital. Between May 27 and October 3, 1853, almost 3,000 yellow fever patients were treated in this hospital. Of that number, some 1,600 died.

teachers were reported absent, but "enough were on the ground[s] to commence the year's education campaign vigorously." This same week observers commented upon the number of new churches going up. Two Methodist churches and one Christian church had already been finished, and the foundations for three others had been laid. One of the latter, Dr. Theodore Clapp's Church of the Messiah, was singled out by the newspapers who described it as a magnificent Gothic edifice. The Reverend Clapp had lost his church by fire in 1851. His devoted congregation, which included some of the wealthiest merchants in town, resolved to provide him with a setting suitable to his talents. The building was not completed until 1855, only two years before Dr. Clapp was forced to retire because of ill health.[22]

On Thursday, October 13, at a meeting of the Board of Health, President Kursheedt proposed a resolution stating that "in the opinion of this Board, the yellow fever has ceased to exist here as an epidemic." The motion was passed unanimously, whereupon Mr. Kursheedt presented a second resolution stating that it was now safe for former residents, but not strangers, to return to the city. Because of the qualification with respect to strangers, this motion was lost. Mr. Kursheedt then offered a third motion that the subcommittee on quarantine maintain the quarantine stations at Fort St. Philip and Fort Jackson in readiness for future use. A substitute motion, which in effect eliminated all quarantine restrictions, proposed that the immigrants in quarantine be sent to New Orleans and that the physicians and all personnel at the quarantine stations be discharged. Over the objections of Mr. Kursheedt, who found himself a minority of one, this substitute motion passed.[23]

The actions of the board were hailed with joy. The *Bee*, a morning paper, which had appeared on the streets before the board had made its decisions, apparently anticipated the result. Its editor pointed out that fifty-eight of the fifty-nine yellow fever deaths the previous week had taken place in Charity Hospital, so that in reality there had been "but one interment from Yellow Fever in the city of New Orleans. A more gratifying indication of the Progressive improvement in our public health," he added, "could not possibly be adduced." The next morning the same paper reported with "heartfelt satisfaction" the news that "upon the authority of the Board of Health" the epidemic was now over. "New Orleans is now perfectly healthy," the editor wrote, "and our absent citizens, whether acclimated or not, may return to the city with perfect safety." Ironically, the day before, in reporting the fifty-nine yellow fever deaths for the previous week, the *Bee* had explained that the fatal cases in Charity Hospital were "persons who had recently arrived here from the interior." The *Picayune* greeted with "profound satisfaction" this "authentic declaration of the entire cessation of the scourge which had been among us." Absent citizens and strangers were informed that their presence was "much needed." The *Crescent*, which echoed the sentiments of the other newspapers, described the weather as pleasant and cool, the city bustling with activity, and business tempo increasing rapidly.[24]

On October 19 the passengers who had been detained in quarantine were brought to New Orleans, where their arrival gave further impetus to the rising spirit of optimism. Three days later Mayor Crossman published a list of contributions received by his office during the course of the epidemic. Over $38,000 had come to the mayor's office, much of it donated by various cities. St. Louis had given over $6,700, Baltimore, $5,600, Washington, D.C., $4,000, Chicago, $4,000, Savannah, $3,400, Nashville, $2,900; and contributions of over $1,000 each had been received from Wheeling, Augusta, and Jersey City. Donations had come from as far as Thomaston, Maine. The lion's share of the $38,000, the amount of $27,500, had been turned over to the Howard Association, and the rest had been contributed to the city's six orphanages and various benevolent societies. Approximately $5,500 remained on hand at the time of reporting, which sum was "to be applied towards the support of those orphaned by the late epidemic." Large as was the figure of $38,000 for its day, it represented only a fraction of the contributions made to New Orleans, for most of the donations were sent directly to the Howard Association rather than to the mayor's office. The Howard Association later reported that it had received approximately $225,000 during the course of the epidemic.[25]

The succeeding days saw a steady influx of new arrivals brought by steamships, riverboats, and railway cars. On October 23 one newspaper expressed amazement at the wonderful change which had taken place during the past two weeks. All evidence shows that "the business pulse of New Orleans is again beating healthily, vigorously and regularly." The large number of steamboats arriving and departing, "the piles of produce which encumber the levee, and the long and incessant processions of drays . . . moving up and down our principal thoroughfares . . ." clearly demonstrate that "our city is again teeming with life and business." [26]

The *Bee* devoted an editorial at this time to extolling the marvelous autumnal weather to be found in New Orleans, comparing it with spring in northern climes. The next day the temperature dropped from 75 to 40 degrees. Unabashed at this change from "the mildest and most genial temperature . . . almost into mid-winter," the *Bee* pointed out that the cool weather had effectually removed "any apprehensions of the lingering presence of Yellow Jack," and had made it possible for anyone to come to New Orleans in perfect security. The amazing revival of the city led the editor to reflect upon the changes which had occurred within the past few weeks. He wrote that he had stood on the corner of Canal and Camp streets at noon on October 24 and had watched the throngs of pedestrians crowding the sidewalks and the businessmen and merchants hurrying along. "As we viewed the constant tide of humanity," he wrote, "borne restlessly along the main artery of New Orleans, we pondered on the signal contrast which it presented in its exuberance of life and motion, with the sluggish, stagnant, silent stream that but a few weeks previously, had slowly crept along that same broad channel. . . ." [27]

The *Picayune* rejoiced at the advent of cool weather, which had brought with it that great adversary of yellow fever, Jack Frost. "Jack Frost is in the ring," proclaimed the newspaper, "and the cruel craven that so lately with savage tyranny struck down high and low, rich and poor, and spared neither age nor sex, will retreat, even from the outskirts and corners to which he had sneaked. . . ." [28] The onset of cold weather was eagerly awaited when yellow fever was present, since it usually meant the end of the epidemic. Precisely why this should be the case was not understood, though it was assumed that frost killed the "fomites" or germs of infection. That insects might have something to do with propagating disease had been suggested, but no one had directly connected yellow fever with mosquitoes.

Despite the felicitous accounts in the daily journals of thriving business activity, the *Price-Current* was under no such illusions. This business journal had been hopeful at the end of September, but it was obvious that the customary seasonal increase in commercial affairs during October was not taking place. Business remained dull, and as late as November 2 the journal reported that "the market has not presented much activity in any department. . . ." A few days later, however, an improvement was noted, though a shortage of shipping was still holding prices down. By November 16 a definite upturn had taken place, and only low water on the western rivers was thought to be holding back economic activity from its normal levels. [29]

In other respects, too, New Orleans was steadily reviving. All Saints

Day, November 1, dawned fine and pleasant, and thousands of citizens made their pilgrimages to the cemeteries. Many of them wore the somber dress of mourning, making a sharp contrast with the bright splashes of color from the flower-strewn graves. Never before had the citizens of New Orleans felt so sharply the losses which occasioned this day of remembrance. The large attendance at the cemeteries greatly increased the traditional collections for the orphans, and for several days after the event, the newspapers carried notices of appreciation from orphanages and benevolent groups. For example, Sister Regis of the Female Orphan Asylum thanked the Portuguese Benevolent Association for $334 collected at the organization's tomb. In her card of thanks she mentioned that there were almost 350 children packed into the asylum. This over-crowding of the orphanages was clearly illustrated in an appeal for funds to establish a new home. The late Alexander Milne had bequeathed $7,000 for this purpose, and the trustees of his estate sought to augment this sum by a public appeal. The *Bee*, editorializing on the subject, re-ferred to the "immense number of orphans" having been thrown upon the charity of existing orphanages and urged private citizens and the state legislature to support the Milne Asylum. "New Asylums," declared its editor, "are among the most urgent wants of our city." [30]

Meanwhile the number of yellow fever deaths was steadily dropping. The week ending November 5 saw only twelve fatalities, ten of them in Charity Hospital. The following week the yellow fever deaths in Char-ity fell to five, and to all intents and purposes the yellow fever outbreak had ended.[31] By the middle of November New Orleans was once again bustling with activity and desperately trying to forget the tragic events of the past months. The amazing vitality of the city aroused wonder throughout the country. The New Orleans newspapers, never exactly shrinking violets on the subject of their city's virtues, were delighted to find this confirmation of their own views and happily reprinted the edi-torials.

A Philadelphia journal declared that it was doubtful if any northern city could have recovered so rapidly from a comparable catastrophe. While paying tribute to the humanitarian spirit of New Orleans, the Philadelphia paper commented upon the thousands of newcomers pour-ing into the city, and in a realistic appraisal of the city's revival, declared: "Commerce has restored the depressed energies of the city, and the struggle for gold more than repairs the damages of death." The Balti-more *American* gave unqualified praise for the manner in which New Orleans had faced the crisis and rebounded from one of the lowest points in its history. The disaster had only "animated the humanity and fired the zeal of its citizens," and "the unconquerable energy of the American character." In any other country, the paper asserted, a city ravaged like New Orleans would not have recovered for years, or might even have been abandoned.[32]

With the yellow fever epidemic rapidly fading into the past, the local papers quickly returned to one of their favorite themes, the relative healthfulness of New Orleans as contrasted with the cities of the North. After comparing the recent bills of mortality for New Orleans and New York, the *Delta* concluded on November 19 that New Orleans was at least as healthy as New York—and this despite the presence of many northerners and "fresh immigrants." In fact, declared the *Delta*, it "is the confident belief of our most experienced and observing physicians that the resident population of New Orleans enjoys a larger share of health and includes more cases of longevity than that of any other city in the Union." [33]

If any doubt remained that the New Orleans newspapers had not returned to normality, the events during the latter half of November settled the matter once and for all. Almost at the moment the yellow fever outbreak had ended, Asiatic cholera made its appearance in New Orleans. On November 24 the Board of Health reported that it had investigated the stories about the presence of cholera and had concluded that there was no cause for alarm. The *Delta* inadvertently let the cat out of the bag while denouncing the "idle rumors circulated by reckless persons." In decrying any possibility of danger, it pointed out that there had been only twenty-two deaths from Asiatic cholera in Charity Hospital since November 1 and that nearly all of the victims were strangers. In the succeeding days all the newspapers, staunchly supported by the Board of Health, expressed righteous indignation at those who would besmirch the city's fair name by implying the presence of a cholera epidemic.[34]

On November 30, the city was shocked to hear of the death of Dr. Abner Hester from Asiatic cholera. Nonetheless, no one was willing to concede that the disease was either epidemic or even likely to become so. To clarify any misunderstanding, Mayor Crossman officially proclaimed on December 10 that despite the reports "of a most injurious character having been circulated . . . relative to the health of New Orleans . . . I deem it my duty to state, for the information of persons abroad, that the health of our city was never better, and that visitors may come to New Orleans with impunity." Ironically, the following day the Board of Health reported a total of 254 deaths for the preceding week, all of which had resulted from Asiatic cholera. Subsequently Hester's journal reported that 607 persons had died from this disease during 1853.[35] In explanation, it should be pointed out that five or six hundred deaths from any one disease was not normally considered an epidemic; nevertheless, the reaction of New Orleans to the Asiatic cholera reveals that the city had completed the full cycle. The brief interval of humility evident in the early fall when editors and public officials were hesitant about dismissing the yellow fever epidemic was obviously only a fleeting sentiment. Having regained its stride, New Orleans was once again resolutely clutching its illusions and warmly contemplating the salubrity of its climate and healthfulness of its people. There was no room for calamity howlers or Jeremiahs in the Crescent City.

There was still some unfinished business related to Street Commissioner James Jolls, who had been the target of vitriolic attacks late in July when the City Council had panicked in the face of the rapidly spreading epidemic. Jolls had remained on the job throughout the crisis, and those councilmen who had fled the city were scarcely in a position to pass a harsh judgment upon any official who had remained at his post. Moreover, all councilmen recognized that the basic fault lay in the system of street sanitation rather than in any personal failings of Mr. Jolls. Under the circumstances, the charges of impeachment were quietly dropped.

CHAPTER VIII

The Widening Circle

New Orleans had long been a focal point for yellow fever, and its appearance there always sent shivers of apprehension through the residents of every seaport and river town in Louisiana, Mississippi, Alabama, and Texas. Mississippi River towns such as Baton Rouge, Natchez, and Vicksburg, and Gulf Coast ports such as Galveston, Biloxi, and Mobile rarely escaped whenever yellow fever ravaged New Orleans. The great epidemic of 1853 was restricted to New Orleans in July and early August; but, despite rigid and extensive quarantine measures, the end of August saw the disease ranging widely throughout the Gulf Coast states. Cases were first reported in Mobile and Natchez in mid-August, and within two weeks the disease had appeared in dozens of Louisiana and Mississippi towns.

Although New Orleans was generally shunned during yellow fever epidemics, the city was never completely shut off from the interior. To close the port of New Orleans was to stifle the economic life of the lower Mississippi Valley; and, in any case, the city needed food and supplies. As local quarantines gradually reduced the amount of goods flowing into the city, prices tended to rise, thus giving added incentive for courageous or greedy entrepreneurs to risk the danger of contracting the disease. Also, because of the well-known immunity of the acclimated residents many rivermen and merchants felt they could visit infected areas with impunity. Thus the constant traffic in and out of the city virtually assured that the disease would spread. Moreover, among the thousands who fled from New Orleans in July, many carried the seeds of infection with them. Had yellow fever been a contact disease, as many people believed, it would certainly have been spread more rapidly and on a much wider front. Fortunately the complex relationship of man and a particular mosquito had a limiting effect on the dissemination of the fever, and most of those who had acquired the virus in New Orleans recovered or died without passing on their disease.

Aside from commercial intercourse and fleeing citizens, there were many other ways by which the pestilence could be carried to adjacent areas. The rising humanitarian impulse of this period led many idealistic young men to go to the assistance of pestilence-plagued areas. For example, on August 17 a group of seven young men from Baton Rouge embarked for New Orleans to offer their services. Bearing a letter from the mayor of Baton Rouge, they presented themselves to Mayor A. D. Crossman. He in turn sent them to Mr. Ricardo, secretary of the Howard Association. Ricardo kindly secured rooms for the group in the St. Charles Hotel and transmitted their offer to the Howard Association. The association regretfully declined because it felt that the young men were not sufficiently acclimated and that remaining in New Orleans would be dangerous for them. The association's decision was wise, for although the group returned to Baton Rouge unscathed, two of the seven died from yellow fever when it subsequently struck Baton Rouge.[1]

The fear engendered by yellow fever in any particular town usually bore a direct relationship to the recency and virulence of previous attacks. Those towns which had borne the brunt of earlier onslaughts were usually the first to erect quarantine barricades. The reputation of yellow fever, however, was all too well known, and its name invariably conjured up the darkest of fears. The panic it aroused was such that a stranger falling prey to the disease might find himself in desperate straits. Early in August a sick engineer from one of the riverboats was landed at Bayou Sara, a small town in West Feliciana Parish. When the proprietor of the boardinghouse in which he was placed discovered that the man had yellow fever, he refused to let him remain. In the middle of the night the patient was removed to a deserted warehouse. The next morning he was able to struggle to the steamboat landing to look for a boat, but the captain of the only available vessel refused to take him on board. In the meantime, the people living in the neighborhood of the warehouse had learned of his disorder and refused to let him return. Going to the original boardinghouse for help, the engineer was then taken to an empty house outside the town limits. Here "a kind gentleman" took care of him, but he died shortly afterwards. To the credit of Louisianians, newspaper reaction to this story was one of shock and outrage, and the treatment afforded this unfortunate individual was certainly not the standard procedure. Yet until the end of the nineteenth century incidents such as this did occur in all sections of the United States.[2]

Understandably, those areas in direct contact with New Orleans were quick to take precautions. Baton Rouge, the first town of any consequence up the river from the Crescent City, was acutely aware of the danger arising from its proximity to New Orleans; and on August 12 one of the local papers criticized the town authorities for failing to provide a suitable hospital for sick travelers. The existing structure was so bad, the journal declared, that it "would be more good Samaritan-like to forbid the landing of such persons." Over and above any philanthropic intent, the hospital was designed to insure that any yellow fever victims landing in town were isolated, thus preventing the fever from gaining a foothold.[3]

On August 13 the Police Jury of the Parish of St. Mary, located to the west of New Orleans, met in response to a petition from the inhabitants to consider "passing an ordinance to prevent the spread of epidemic and contagious diseases." In short order, the police jury established a Board of Health and provided for the election "of a regularly licensed physician to be known as Parish Health Officer." The police jury ordered that the health officer be stationed at Lynch's Point, at the junction of Grand Lake and the Atchafalaya River, where he was to board all vessels and examine the crew and passengers. No vessel could proceed, nor could any persons land, without a certificate from the health officer. Vessels coming from infected areas could not pass down the Atchafalaya, even when the crew and passengers were in good health, unless nine days had elapsed since their leaving the infected port.[4]

Having protected the northern and western approaches to the town, the Board of Health shortly thereafter stationed another health officer at the mouth of the Atchafalaya on Berwick Bay to guard against any infection coming by sea. The citizens of the parish were determined to enforce their quarantine. On August 24 a steamboat from New Orleans refused to stop at one of the quarantine stations. When word reached Franklin, the parish seat, the Court House bell sounded the alarm and citizens carrying rifles, muskets, and shotguns poured down to the banks of Bayou Teche and forced the vessel to turn about. Two days later a similar situation developed with the United States mail boat. A passenger had come directly from New Orleans, and the steamer was held up overnight until the captain consented to deliver him over to the quarantine authorities. Immediately following this last incident, the citizens, at a mass meeting, declared it their intention to arm themselves if necessary to enforce the health regulations. It was further resolved "that a train band be forthwith organized, consisting of at least thirty men, to be duly armed and equipped, and subject to be called into service at a moment's notice. . . ." [5]

Meanwhile in dozens of towns in Louisiana and the other Gulf Coast states, municipal councils and police juries were taking similar steps. Quarantine stations were being set up and temporary boards of health were beginning to function. While St. Mary Parish may have been a little more zealous than some areas, the general pattern was much the same. By this time Natchez, Vicksburg, Biloxi, Mobile, Houston, and Galveston had all taken precautions. Galveston and Houston, for example, required all vessels from infected areas to spend fifteen days in quarantine. Cargoes had to be exposed to the air and fumigated before they could be discharged, and passengers wishing to land were compelled to spend an additional five days in quarantine. Natchez and Vicksburg, long noted for the stringency of their quarantine regulations, put them into effect shortly after hearing of the New Orleans epidemic; but in 1853, here as elsewhere, nothing seemed to stay the dreaded yellow scourge.[6]

The first communities to feel the weight of the disease were those adjacent to New Orleans. In suburbs such as Algiers and Carrollton, the case and mortality rates were as bad if not worse than in the city itself. A brief newspaper item on August 14 mentioned that Algiers, a small town directly across the river from New Orleans, with a population of sixteen hundred, had suffered forty-two deaths from yellow fever in one week! The little town of Gretna was no better off; on September 5 the *Delta* mentioned that it had lost seventy-five out of a population of five hundred, a 15 percent loss! The disease hit in these places a little later than in New Orleans but followed the same general course.[7]

Baton Rouge, only eighty miles away on a direct route but much further by way of the winding Mississippi River, managed to avoid yellow fever until the end of August. With the first news of yellow fever the city and parish officials had enforced their quarantine measures and hoped for the best. All went well for several weeks, but by the end of August it became evident that the quarantine had failed. The first clue to this was an editorial in the *Daily Comet* asserting that all rumors to the contrary, Baton Rouge, "at this season of the year, was never more healthy." The following day the paper ridiculed one of the other news-paper editors for reporting a yellow fever case and accused him of causing needless trouble. Two days later its editor admitted that there had been a few more deaths than usual, but it saw "no occasion for alarm." Significantly, the editor did suggest dispensing with the tolling of the church bells for the funeral of "every man, woman and child." By this time the existence of yellow fever was indisputable, and on September 5 the city authorities established a Board of Health "to furnish for publication, daily, a correct statement of the number of deaths occurring within the limits of this Corporation. . . ." [8]

The first daily mortality report, on September 6, showed three yellow fever deaths, and its publication threw the whole city into panic. Within fifteen minutes after the *Comet*'s issue of Thursday, September 7, reached the streets with a report of yellow fever deaths, "there was a rush to the livery stables, and all kinds of vehicles were brought into immediate service. . . ." While deploring the panic, the editor reluctantly advised all people "to scatter into the country as fast as they can." Heedless of danger, the editor and staff remained at their posts. Throughout the epidemic they faithfully reported the daily deaths, urged the citizens to organize for the relief of the indigent sick, and alternately praised and condemned city officials. Within two weeks, approximately forty yellow fever deaths had been recorded. Among the victims, as mentioned earlier, were two of the seven young men who had volunteered their services to New Orleans. All seven elected to remain in Baton Rouge when the crisis came, and their example helped tide the city over the first crucial days.[9]

As the number of cases mounted, constant appeals were made for nurses and servants. To make matters worse, within three weeks after the outbreak, the deaths of Dr. L. Vary and Dr. C. Adams and the sickness of Dr. Ludlow, Dr. Lowry, and Dr. Williams created a serious shortage of trained medical personnel. Fortunately, as the New Orleans epidemic was tapering off, the Howard Association began sending doctors and nurses to towns and cities needing help. On Thursday, September 22, at the request of Captain William F. Tunnard, secretary of the Baton Rouge Board of Health, six nurses and two physicians arrived from New Orleans. They could scarcely have come at a more propitious time, for Baton Rouge was at the peak of the outbreak. Shortly thereafter, however, the number of cases began to drop, and by October 1, the Board of Health was able to announce that the epidemic was rapidly abating.[10]

Baton Rouge was the site of a United States Army post containing some 110 service men. Since the majority of these were from northern states, yellow fever found a fertile field for its activities. In the period from August 23 to October 1, there were 73 cases of yellow fever and 13 deaths recorded. Thus within five to six weeks two-thirds of the garrison sickened and 12 percent lost their lives. As October drew on, the number of yellow fever deaths within the army post and the city fell off sharply, and after October 15 the newspapers no longer published the daily mortality figures. On October 19 the *Comet* dismissed the epidemic and sought to dispel the impression which "prevails abroad that the pestilence still lingers about this place." The editor wrote with confidence that there "is not a more healthy point on the Mississippi than Baton Rouge." Moreover, he added, nearly all of the two hundred victims in Baton Rouge had been strangers who had permitted "a light grade of billious fever . . . to degenerate" into yellow fever for want of proper nursing and medical attention.[11]

Both in the premature announcement of the cessation of the epidemic and in the bland dismissal of two hundred deaths on the grounds that the victims were strangers, the editor of the *Comet* was behaving true to form. Local pride was as strong in Baton Rouge as it was in any other town or city; and although the inhabitants of any particular community might take occasional perverse pleasure in denouncing their weather, they were the last to admit the possibility that their locality was not a health spa. Fortunately, the Baton Rouge Board of Health was more realistic and responded to the editor's assertions by issuing an official notice declaring it still unsafe to return to or visit the city. The wisdom of the board's action was shown by the announcement of four yellow fever deaths on Tuesday, October 25, a week after the *Comet* had proclaimed an end to the epidemic. And it was the second week in November before the last cases of yellow fever cleared up, the schools opened, and the city returned to normality.[12]

In Baton Rouge the yellow fever had lurked for several weeks before bursting out on an epidemic scale. In many other places the disease struck with virtually no warning. A case in point was the small town of Thibodaux, where a sudden and devastating outbreak caused most residents to flee in panic and decimated those who remained. The first real inkling of events came on September 10 when a number of Louisiana newspapers picked up a brief statement by J. C. White, editor of the Thibodaux *Minerva*. On the "mail bill" for September he had written: "Stores closed—town abandoned—151 cases yellow fever—twenty-two deaths—Postmaster absent—clerks all down with the Fever." Subsequently, the *Southern Sentinel*, a Plaquemine newspaper, republished an item from the *Minerva* dated Thursday, September 8, stating that thirty-four deaths had already occurred that week.[13]

In one of the most graphic of all accounts of a yellow fever epidemic, Mr. White wrote that there was "a panic amongst our citizens verging on frenzy." All business concerns were closed, he continued, and the deserted streets looked more like paths in "the wilderness than the public thoroughfares of a thriving commercial town of 1500 inhabitants." In recounting the events of the preceding two weeks, Mr. White said that up to August 27 there had been twenty-two cases, but the number had then taken a sudden upturn. When one of the newspaper's employees had come down with yellow fever, the rest had fled. By Saturday, September 3, over 160 persons were desperately ill, and a mass exodus of the well had already taken place. "Never," wrote the editor, "have we witnessed scenes of greater distress and abandonment of fear." Parents, he said, were deserting their children, and children were forsaking their parents, leaving them "to the protection of benevolent strangers." [14]

The next word from Thibodaux came from the assistant postmaster who reported on September 9: "Yellow Fever still raging; two hundred sick; seventy deaths up to this morning. . . . Hardly enough of us well to take care of the sick." As word of Thibodaux's plight spread, the Howard Association in New Orleans quickly made arrangements to send help, and on September 15 one of its members, well equipped with medicines and supplies and accompanied by Dr. C. H. Porter and several nurses, left for Thibodaux. With this assistance Thibodaux weathered the crisis, but it was the end of October before the town was entirely free of sickness.[15]

A similar attack occurred in the town of Washington, in St. Landry Parish. This particular outbreak has significance both in itself and for its effect on the neighboring community of Opelousas. As with so many serious epidemics, the first reference to yellow fever was a solemn denial of its existence. On August 29, in response to the rumored presence of yellow fever, a public meeting of the citizens was held at which a citizens committee was appointed. After consulting with local physicians, the committee announced "that there had not been *less* sickness in the town at this season of the year for many years. . . ." True, a single death had occurred from yellow fever, and a young man had been sick for eleven days with symptoms resembling the disease, but there was no evidence that the fever had spread. It was completely at a loss, the committee stated, to "account for the various injurious and totally false reports which have been freely circulated," and it could not denounce "in too strong terms" those responsible for such untruths.[16]

Two weeks later the Opelousas *Courier* reported general panic because of yellow fever "raging awfully" in neighboring Washington. Of Washington itself, nothing further was heard until a letter, dated September 25, managed to pass the quarantine barricades. The writer, a Captain Hinkley, wrote that the town had buried fifty-nine persons within the past three weeks and that he personally knew of "70 sick in their beds." Everyone who could had fled from town. All business had ceased and nothing was being done save "coffin-making and grave-digging, and hard work to get men to do that," for we can "muster but *eleven* well men in the whole town. God only knows," he concluded, "where this will end." [17]

In the meantime the New Orleans Howard Association had responded to appeals for help. A physician and two nurses were dispatched on September 23 but were unable to reach Washington. In order to avoid local quarantines, they took a circuitous route requiring them to take passage on a mail boat on Lake Verret. Unfortunately, this latter vessel ran aground, and, after awaiting repairs for forty-eight hours, during which time they had no place to sleep and little to eat, they finally had no choice but to return to New Orleans. Mr. E. L. Nimmo of the Howard Association explained all this in a letter to the Opelousas *Courier* written on September 26. He added that he was sending a new expedition, consisting of a doctor and several nurses, which would go to the Atchafalaya River "and from thence in a canoe or skiff to the mouth of the Little Devil, 25 miles." Here they would obtain men and boats from the "steam-boat Opelousas (now repairing)," to take them up the Courtableau, forty miles, to Washington, "and thereby escape the Big Boiler or cannon of the Quarantine and shot guns, and oaths, by the Attakapas mail route." [18]

Although fever was still raging in Washington on October 1, cool weather set in during the following week and was credited with sharply reducing the number of cases. The rigid quarantine established by the citizens of Opelousas against Washington was raised on October 6, and within a few more days Washington was clear of the disease.[19] In recapitulating the course of the outbreak, it is clear that yellow fever was present in Washington at the time of the citizens' mass meeting on August 29, but because of the ten or twelve days incubation period before the infected mosquito can transmit the disease and the normal human incubation period, the citizens had assumed that the danger from the two previous cases had passed.

Subsequent investigation revealed that the first case was that of a stranger who had come from New Orleans on August 12. He already showed symptoms of yellow fever on his arrival, and the town authorities had removed him several miles into the country. The next case was not diagnosed until August 29, but a few days earlier the man's brother had died of a "bad fever." It was at this time, when the infected mosquitoes were becoming capable of passing on the virus, that the epidemic broke out with explosive force. The resultant exodus reduced the inhabitants of Washington to about four hundred and those of Opelousas to about five hundred. Many of those fleeing Washington carried the disease with them out into the parish, but, fortunately, because of a lack of the *Aedes aegypti* or for other reasons, the fever did not become general. A writer reviewing the epidemic at the end of the year estimated that there had been about four hundred cases, all of which, with the exception of one or two, had originated in Washington. Approximately one hundred of those infected succumbed to the disease, a serious loss for so small a town.[20]

Although Opelousas escaped yellow fever, its reaction to the Washington outbreak clearly illustrates the disruptive influence of the presence of yellow fever. News of its onslaught on Washington literally terrified the residents of Opelousas. On September 5, a day or two after yellow fever became manifest in Washington, Opelousas established a *Cordon Sanitaire* around itself. When two residents who had visited Washington prior to the quarantine fell sick of yellow fever, the town panicked. The editor of the *Courier* wrote on September 17 that only those who could not afford to leave were still in town. About forty families had already left "with tents, baggages, provisions. &c." for the Bell Cheney and Beaver Creek springs, the banks of the Teche and the Whiskychitto, and other isolated areas. Among those who left were the editor and staff of the St. Landry *Whig*, a competitor of the *Courier*. When the *Whig* later criticized the *Courier*, the editor of the latter was quick to point out this fact. A week later, on September 24, the *Courier* editor again spoke of the general panic, the like of which he had never seen before. More than three-fourths of the homes are abandoned, nearly all stores closed, and the neighboring planters have forbidden their slaves to come among "us with vegetables, milk, &c.," he wrote in despair. And yet, other than the death of the two yellow fever cases which originated in Washington, "our town has never been so healthy, during this season of the year." [21]

The Washington-Opelousas situation showed another of the peculiarities of yellow fever. The epidemic in Washington definitely was traced to the arrival of a case from New Orleans, thus justifying the quarantine established by Opelousas. But two yellow fever patients who had contracted their disease in Washington returned to Opelousas, were given medical care, and yet the disease did not gain a foothold. This was one of the most confounding aspects of yellow fever. Time after time epidemics were started by the arrival of one case, but just as frequently, no dire results might ensue. It was this sporadic fashion with which yellow fever struck, seemingly at random, which added to its horror and precipitated stampedes such as occurred in Opelousas. In one sense, the wholesale exodus from communities, by reducing the population density, may well have prevented epidemic outbreaks, or at least may have limited the fever's depredations where it already existed.

The grim experience of the residents of Baton Rouge, Thibodaux, and Washington was repeated in dozens of other towns and villages in Louisiana and the surrounding states. Panic, abandonment of homes, and disruption of all normal activities were standard reactions to the threat of yellow fever. Whenever the pestilence chose to strike, a heavy loss of life was certain to ensue. From late August to the end of October, the fever ranged throughout the Gulf states. It followed the multitudinous waterways of Louisiana to scourge towns far in the interior, while refugees from New Orleans carried the disease into every resort area along the Gulf Coast and on the northern shores of Lake Pontchartrain. The *Aedes aegypti* mosquito had already pushed its way into most settled areas, and the ground was prepared for an epidemic once the fever was introduced. Quarantine measures could and often did prove effective in keeping the disorder out of particular areas, but in many instances incipient yellow fever patients had already entered the community before the quarantine was put into effect. Moreover, infected mosquitoes in the cabins and holds of steamers could easily nullify the quarantine efforts.

One of the brighter aspects of the New Orleans epidemic was the universal sympathy it evoked, and, more tangibly, the strong financial support it received from all quarters. All told, over $200,000 poured into New Orleans, and dozens of young doctors appeared on the scene, most of whom were inspired by a genuine wish to be of service. Equally notable was the work of the Howard Association and the many benevolent groups which dedicated themselves to caring for yellow fever victims. The credit is all the greater considering that most of the sick were newcomers or strangers, and the majority of these belonged to what was generally termed the "dissolute poor." The membership of the volunteer groups came primarily from the middle and upper classes, and it must have taken a great deal of character and fortitude for them to enter the filthy hovels of the poor. Indeed, their contact with yellow fever victims may well have been their first awakening to social injustice. In coming face to face with the individual poor, certainly some of these middle class humanitarians must have realized for the first time that poverty arose as much from a brutalizing environment as from any weakness of character.

Whatever may have been the social implications of the philanthropic spirit engendered by the yellow fever epidemic, once the crisis was passed, the New Orleans Howard Association moved promptly to extend its sphere of activities to other towns needing help. Responding to every appeal, and in some cases not even waiting for an appeal, Howard members showed up in cities, towns, and villages all the way from Texas to Alabama. In larger communities the Howard members, acting as resource personnel, organized local relief groups, determined medical needs, and coordinated the health program. Doctors and nurses from New Orleans usually accompanied or preceded the Howard members, and where they were needed, medical supplies, blankets, linens, and money were brought into the community. Thus it was that many communities which had contributed to the relief of New Orleans during August found their roles reversed, as relief contingents from the city returned their generosity with interest in September and October.

The epidemic had scarcely begun to wane in New Orleans when the Howard Association began to extend its work. One of the first communities to benefit was Mobile, Alabama, a town which may have borne relatively heavier yellow fever losses than New Orleans. The fever began there early in August and reached its peak about a month later. For the week ending August 26, there were 37 yellow fever deaths reported. The next week this figure jumped to 156, and the following week, ending September 9, it reached 194. It was about this time that the New Orleans Howard Association came to the rescue. At the end of August the mayor of Mobile received word from the Howard Association that in view of Mobile's own need, all funds contributed by Mobile to New Orleans would be returned and that the association was prepared to render any assistance needed. On September 11 a Mobile newspaper reported that D. I. Ricardo and J. E. Caldwell of the New Orleans Howard Association had visited the city to inspect the infirmaries and evaluate general conditions, and had informed the mayor's office that they were ready to provide money, doctors, and nurses.[22]

In the meantime the Howard Association had notified various New Orleans relief committees, such as the one in New York, that New Orleans was no longer in need of funds and advised them to transfer their financial support to Mobile.[23] Although the Howard Association could help to alleviate distress and mitigate suffering, it could do nothing to stay the course of the Mobile epidemic, which inexorably burned its way through the remaining population. By the middle of October it was rapidly dying down, although it was not until October 26 that the Board of Health officially proclaimed the epidemic at an end. From August 1 to October 26, the official number of yellow fever deaths was 889, though the Mobile *Advertiser* estimated that the true number of yellow fever victims was 1,072. Considering that another of the local newspapers placed the mean population at 8,500 and that many of these had fled with the onset of yellow fever, Mobile quite literally was decimated by the outbreak.[24]

In Houston, Galveston, and other Texas towns, the fever arrived toward the end of August, reached its peak late in September, and steadily diminished in intensity until its disappearance around the beginning of November. In Mississippi and Alabama the disease followed a similar pattern but started its deadly work sooner. It began early in August, reached its peak a month later, and then gradually declined until the end of October. Throughout all of these states quarantines of varying effectiveness were enforced by local authorities. In some instances the quarantine successfully held the pestilence at bay; in others it proved no barrier at all, and the net effect was to add to the confusion and to intensify the great debates over the validity of quarantine measures. The members of the Howard Association, for all their experience, made no attempt to pass judgment on the cause of yellow fever nor to become involved in the heated arguments concerning it. Abstract debates held no appeal for them while people were sick and dying. How or why yellow fever struck a particular community was a question they were willing to leave to the medical and scientific world; the Howard Association's concern was with mitigating the effects of yellow fever wherever it appeared.

The cool weather of November was well at hand before the labors of the Howard members ceased, and the association was able to draw up an accounting of its activities. In New Orleans alone it had cared for 11,088 yellow fever patients. Of these 2,942 had died, largely because many were beyond help before they came to the attention of the Howard members. To care for this vast number of patients, the association, starting on July 14, had received almost $229,000, an incredible sum for that day. In all, disbursements totaled about $163,000, leaving a balance as of December 1 of $66,000 to be held in reserve for future emergencies.[25]

The breakdown of expenditures shows that New Orleans accounted for the bulk of the money spent. The next largest expense arose in connection with the aid to many other Louisiana communities suffering from the pestilence. Of the money spent outside Louisiana, the chief beneficiaries were Mobile, $1,800; Galveston, $1,000; Indianola, Texas, $750; and Jackson, Mississippi, $680. Of the total expenditures, medical care accounted for the largest part, with provisions, $30,000, coming second. This latter heading, "Provisions," which included "Groceries, Meat, Poultry, Vegetables, Soups, Ice, Bread, Brandy, Wine, Porter, Ale, &c.," provides a fine commentary upon the medical prescriptions of the day. Another $11,000 was distributed to five orphanages. In passing, the association noted that in addition to establishing three temporary orphanages and caring for 241 children, it had also employed wet nurses for 97 small babies.[26]

The year 1853 was one in which the sectional crisis was growing. In the halls of Congress, in newspapers and magazines, and in campaign oratory everywhere, bitter denunciations and recriminations were being hurled by extremists in both the North and South. Yet when news of the disaster in New Orleans spread through the land, sectional differences were forgotten; from every part of America, from every level of society, assistance came pouring into the plague-stricken city. Private charity, which had functioned quite well in a simple rural society, still continued, and, as an impersonal urban civilization was developing, a new humanitarian spirit had begun to flourish. The concept of governmental responsibility for human welfare was only just evolving and lagged far behind urban and industrial development. Private benevolence bridged the gap until local government could grow up to its responsibilities. The Howard Association, aided by smaller voluntary groups, became a "government" within a government. It created a strong centralized administration, hired its own doctors, nurses, and pharmacists, purchased thousands of dollars worth of food, medicines, bedding, and clothing, rented buildings and halls and turned them into temporary hospitals, convalescent infirmaries, and orphanages, and conducted a highly successful drive for funds.

Despite their incessant labors under the worst of conditions, not one of the original thirty Howard members nor their assistants was attacked by yellow fever, a fact which gave firm proof to the assumption that acclimated residents of New Orleans were perfectly safe from the yellow scourge. Their faith in their invulnerability to the pestilence in no way detracts from their remarkable contributions. Whatever motives they may have had—Christian charity, human compassion, or an intelligent recognition of human interdependence—the actions of the Howard Association members and all who supported them gave proof of man's ability to rise above himself. History is all too full of instances of man's inhumanity to man; those citizens of New Orleans who remained to fight the plague demonstrated that the human spirit, which too often descends to the depth of degradation, is also capable of achieving Olympian heights.

From the standpoint of the development of American institutions, it is significant that the success of voluntary groups in dealing with the crises in New Orleans and other cities helped to foster the concept of volunteer action and direct citizen participation. Had the Howard Association not stepped into the picture, municipal officials would undoubtedly have widened the scope of their activities, but it is unlikely that in 1853 they could have accomplished nearly so much. It is true, however, that a series of disastrous epidemics of yellow fever and Asiatic cholera helped to extend the powers of local and state governments and led to an increasing assumption of responsibility on their part.

Successful as was the work of the Howard Association, the growing recognition of the need to prevent rather than mitigate epidemic diseases precipitated the establishment of some permanent organizations. By the end of the nineteenth century, the creation of health boards and other governmental agencies had gradually eliminated the need for organizations such as the Howard Association. They had made a real contribution to society, however, and as needs changed and new challenges emerged, other volunteer agencies came into existence. These groups continued to carve out new spheres of action, and their roles were never completely supplanted. Henceforth voluntary groups continued to be an integral part of the advancing front of public health.

CHAPTER IX

Aftermath

EVEN AS THE EPIDEMIC raged, newspapers and medical journals had speculated at length upon the nature and cause of yellow fever. A wide variety of theories was set forth, but the major issue around which the debate centered was the question of contagion versus sanitation; that is, was yellow fever a specific infection introduced into the city or was it a disease spontaneously generated in dirt and filth. But far more significant to the people of New Orleans than theoretical considerations was the practical matter of what could be done to prevent or mitigate any recurrence of the pestilence. The shameful condition of the streets and the criminal negligence of the City Council in failing to establish a board of health until the victims of yellow fever already numbered in the hundreds were issues still sharply etched in the consciousness of those who lived through the terrible summer of 1853.

In September the New Orleans newspapers drew the attention of their readers to the prevailing theories about yellow fever and called for a thorough investigation of the current outbreak. The *Bee* quoted at length from a medical writer who sought to disprove the contagiousness of yellow fever by citing the example of Philadelphia. The author noted that although this city had suffered heavily from the disorder in its early history, virtually no cases had appeared there for more than twenty years. Since Philadelphia's population had grown rapidly and the number of vessels entering the port from yellow fever areas had increased commensurately, the writer asserted that "the fair inference from this fact is that it cannot be, and that it never was imported." Furthermore, it was his opinion that the banishment of the disease from Philadelphia could only be attributed to the improved sanitary condition of the city and the "universal introduction of the Schuykill water." [1]

In a series of editorials, the *Picayune* called for a comprehensive study of the prevailing epidemic and for a 2-pronged attack upon the causal factors. In addition to a thorough cleansing of the city and a close regulation of sewage disposal, cesspools, construction, and all public and private buildings, the journal demanded that the swamp in the rear of the city be drained and the land reclaimed, so as to destroy the miasmas and mosquitoes and to permit the introduction of the healthful breezes from Lake Pontchartrain. On the quarantine issue, it wisely suggested that since the medical profession and the public were divided as to whether yellow fever was of domestic or foreign origin, the city authorities adopt both sanitary and quarantine measures. Until it has been demonstrated "that no malignant disease is communicable," argued the *Picayune*, "it is the duty of every large seaport town to maintain quarantine." If it should be proven that yellow fever is imported, no harm will have been done by the "efficient enforcement of internal sanitary measures . . . no one will be found to complain of his inability to behold reeking heaps of offal, the putrefying carcasses of dead horses, dogs, cats, rats, &c., stagnant pools of foul water, and all the innumerable genera of eyesores." [2]

Partly in response to public demand and partly motivated by a genuine desire to find a rational explanation for the holocausts of fever which periodically swept through New Orleans, on September 26 the Board of Health appropriated $2,500 for the use of a proposed 5-man sanitary commission to study all aspects of the prevailing epidemic. In an era of argument and debate and of charges and countercharges, even the membership of the commission became the subject of a hot discussion. According to the resolution of the Board of Health, Mayor Crossman appointed five doctors, A. Foster Axson, Edward H. Barton, J. C. Simonds, John L. Riddell, and S. D. McNeil to the commission. All five were outstanding medical men: Axson was a crusading editor; Barton was a leading figure in the Louisiana public health movement who had joined with Dr. Simonds in an effort to awaken the people of New Orleans to their incredibly high death rate and generally deplorable sanitary condition; Riddell was professor of chemistry in the medical school; and McNeil was a well-known practitioner.[3]

The *Delta* published a long editorial regretting that only the medical profession was represented on the commission. "Besides the natural tendency of doctors to disagree," wrote the editor, "this subject of yellow fever has been peculiarly the bone of contention of the Faculty, scarcely any two concurring in the main points of the nature and history." The medical profession has deluged the world with publications on yellow fever and "every youthful son of Esculapius" has written a pamphlet or book. Having set forth his views, the editorial continued, every physician "is bound to sustain them." Conceding that the men on the commission were all of high calibre, "still they are all doctors, and on this subject, the people view with some suspicion, all medical testimony." The editor deprecated the popular view that "the opinions of doctors on sanitary subjects are entitled to but little confidence, because they are pecuniarily interested in the existence of epidemics," but he thought it would be better to have some other professions represented on a commission designed to report "upon the facts of this epidemic." While he would not exclude doctors from the commission, he did feel they should be a minority. "This is necessary," he asserted, "to secure the popular confidence for the report which may be made." [4]

A few days later the *Crescent* defended the membership of the commission. Although the journal had opposed many decisions of the Board of Health, such as stirring up the "feculented mud and stagnant water from the gutters and ditches," the terrible roar of the cannon at nightfall, and the burning of gunpowder, which filled "the gloomy chambers of the sick with startling sounds, villainous smells, and suffocating volumes of smoke," it felt that the board's decision to turn to the medical faculty was a wise one. [5]

Individual members of the medical profession, however, did not share the *Crescent's* confidence in the profession's collective wisdom. Dr. M. Morton Dowler, an able physician and a brother of Bennet Dowler, an editor of the *New Orleans Medical & Surgical Journal*, commended the *Delta* for its stand. Taking a sly dig at Barton and Simonds, who had attempted to demonstrate by mortality statistics that New Orleans was anything but a health spa, Dr. Dowler asserted that few people really knew anything about the city's health and that the mortuary statistics offered no help. Dowler, an ardent adversary of quarantine, was apprehensive—correctly as it turned out—that the members of the commission would favor quarantine measures, and he turned his major attack in this direction. Hitting at Barton and Simonds again, he declared that yellow fever was present in New Orleans every summer, but that no one had been permitted to announce its existence "till the *counting-house physicians* have declared the epidemic. . . ." It would be unworthy of the enlightened and intelligent people of New Orleans to restore the "old Fogyism" of quarantine for yellow fever, since "quarantine would have about the same control over the Northeast wind, as over this disease." Dowler's fears of quarantine were fully justified. Three days later in an editorial urging the establishment of a permanent board of health, one of the newspapers virtually equated an effective health board with strict quarantine measures.[6]

Despite initial criticism, the Sanitary Commission swung into action promptly. Inquiries were sent to all major cities and agencies of the federal government, and questionnaires were distributed to members of the medical profession and to many private citizens. The commission then set itself up as "a Court of Inquiry" for three months, "eliciting and inviting information from every accessible source." While the commission was beginning its work, the newspapers began a campaign to pressure the city council into establishing a permanent board of health. The *Picayune*, in noting that the common council would resume its weekly sessions on October 11, strongly urged immediate action.[7] At its first meeting the council appointed a special committee under the leadership of Assistant Alderman Starke to contact eminent physicians on the city's health needs. On October 18 Mr. Starke reported that Dr. Wederstrandt, Dr. Axson, Dr. LeMonnier, and Dr. McCormick had recommended establishing an underground drainage system, enlarging the waterworks, paving the streets with smooth square blocks, draining the low land around the city, and constructing municipal houses for bathing, washing, and ironing.

On the basis of its correspondence with physicians, Mr. Starke's committee proposed an ordinance establishing a city health department "to take cognizance of all matters and subjects pertaining to the public health." The director or health officer was to be given broad powers enabling him to remove all nuisances—"putrid and unsound meat, . . . hides or skins, all dead animals, and every putrid, offensive, unsound or unwholesome substance found in any street, alley, yard, dwelling, ditch or canal, or the eddies of the river." He could inspect all privies and cesspools and require that they be built or altered in accordance with the law. He was authorized to regulate the dumping of all substances along the shores or in the river, and to enter and examine any premises between sunrise and sunset. He was to be responsible for inspecting all tenement houses and could levy fines against owners who overcrowded their buildings. Lastly he was to have control over cemeteries and was to be responsible for publishing a weekly bill of mortality. The Board of Assistant Aldermen deferred action upon the proposals for a health

A crowded burial ground near the Metairie Race Course. New Orleans cemeteries could not accommodate the daily death tolls of nearly three hundred.

department, but it quickly adopted a resolution by Mr. Starke to establish a quarantine station.[8]

Following the action of the Board of Assistant Aldermen, the proposal for a quarantine station was promptly submitted to the Board of Aldermen, but this group had no intention of being rushed into precipitate action—or any other kind of action for that matter! Although the epidemic was virtually ended, some of the members had been in no haste to return to New Orleans, and others, for various reasons, were submitting their resignations. It is possible that several of the councilmen may have been reluctant to face the voters after their cowardice in fleeing the city during the summer crisis, but, for whatever reasons, there was a long delay in achieving a quorum of the Board of Aldermen.

In the meantime several of the newspapers, following the lead of the *Picayune*, began a strenuous campaign in favor of a quarantine system. The *Picayune* editor, seeking to counter the views of physicians who were much opposed to quarantine laws, wrote a long editorial on science and professional men in which he sought to differentiate between the results of science and the hypotheses of science. Professional men, he said, were prone to assume that their hypotheses were facts. Under the circumstances, the editor asked, was it not "much safer to follow the common sense and unbiased opinion of the intelligent mass of the people than the opinions of medical men . . . based upon hypothetical theories." While he was perfectly willing to accept medical treatment from a physician, he saw no reason why he should give "full credence to the physician's hypothesis of the origin of the disease." Quarantine, which could do little harm and might possibly do infinite good, the editor concluded, properly belonged to the art of public health rather than medicine.[9]

Since the entire state had been aroused over the yellow fever threat, proponents of sanitary reform were quite concerned over the election of state legislators on November 7. The *Commercial Bulletin*, a Whig paper, declared on November 1 that sanitary regulations for the state and city would be the major issue confronting the legislature. Regardless of the merits of such a program, the newspaper stated, unless New Orleans established a rigid system of sanitation in the summer months, she would find herself cut off from the entire interior of the United States. In the eyes of this journal the issue was whether it was better for New Orleans to cut off communications with certain yellow fever areas during the critical months or to find herself cut off from the rest of the United States. The following day another paper commented rather cynically: "Save us all from such sanitary measures as the Legislature will enact." [10]

Meanwhile the City Council was slowly mulling over the proposal to create a health department. On November 20 the *Picayune* asked: "What has become of the system of sanitary measures which was introduced with such creditable expedition into the Board of Assistant Aldermen at its first session this fall?" If the proposal is "to be suffered to slumber indefinitely upon the table of the Council," all advantage of its early introduction will be lost. Stirred into action, two days later the Board of Assistant Aldermen discussed the proposed health ordinance at length and approved a resolution calling for a health officer at $6,000 per year, a deputy health officer at $2,000, and a clerk at $1,200. The *Crescent*, unduly suspicious of a City Council dominated by the Democratic party, claimed that the movement to establish a health department was simply a device to create political patronage. The whole proposal was an effort by council members who expect to go out of office next April to "take care that they shall not go unprovided for during the two years to come. The attempt to fasten such an abomination on the city," proclaimed the *Crescent* with indignation, "should meet the loud and unqualified reprobation of every member of the community." [11]

The editor of the *Crescent* was needlessly alarmed, since the council was moving at its usual imperceptible pace. On November 30 the Board of Assistant Aldermen met and took up as the first order of business "the expediency of establishing a 'Health Department'." In the words of a reporter for the *Bee*: "Some members were energetic and warm in advocating its necessity, while others denounced it as a 'delusion and snare.' As there are medical and legal gentlemen connected with the Council, we can only say, in the language of the adage, 'Who shall decide when Doctors disagree?' " Throughout the succeeding weeks the assistant aldermen continued to debate the various provisions of the health ordinance. Although nearly all of the newspapers supported the measure in principle, they were as divided as the council on the individual sections of the ordinance. For example, the *Picayune*, one of the staunchest advocates of a health department, strongly objected when it was proposed to create a board of health made up of five physicians. The *Picayune* felt that a larger board, "selected from various callings of life" and acting without salaries, would be more efficient and would be likely to receive greater public confidence.[12]

On December 22, the *Bee* excoriated the councilmen. "Our city fa-

thers," the editor began, "seem to have a holy horror of the improvement
of public health, and a suspicious affection for the various groggeries
and rum holes of the city." This had been demonstrated, said the editor, by the council rejecting both Mr. Starke's plan for a health department and a petition to prevent the use of grog shops as polling
places. The editor agreed that Mr. Starke's original proposal had been
too cumbersome and would have placed inordinate powers in the hands
of the health commissioner. But, he went on to say, the resolution could
have been simplified "and modified so as to make it acceptable to the
community. No one will deny that if our city is to be protected from
future epidemic visitations, its hygienic condition should be made the
subject of unremitting and authorized supervision." The fact that the
cleanest cities, such as Philadelphia, Boston, and Charleston, were also
the healthiest "is an unanswerable argument to those who question the
morbific tendencies of accumulated filth." The editor concluded that
since Mr. Starke's proposal had been shelved, it was to be hoped some
other member would undertake to draft a simple, concise, and acceptable version of it.[13]

Although the papers continued to harp on the subject of the city's
health needs, as the weeks passed with nothing accomplished, interest
again turned to the state legislature. Early in January, the *Picayune*
sponsored a petition to the legislature urging the creation of a quarantine system. In the meantime the legislature itself had appointed a joint
committee to investigate the recurrent epidemics. Like the Sanitary
Commission, the legislative committee began its task by sending a
questionnaire to the doctors of New Orleans, but it received little cooperation. The committee consoled itself with the thought that the
failure of the physicians to respond was not too great a loss, since the
few who "deemed the subject worthy of their consideration . . . [did]
not agree together." The joint committee members themselves were
unable to agree upon a final report. The result was the issuance of a majority and a minority report. In general the committee sought a middle
ground position in which it advocated both sanitation and quarantine.
It expressed the belief that the severity of the 1853 epidemic had resulted from the fact that "the ordinary yellow fever was modified by
the presence of Typhus." As a concession to the sanitationists, the committee declared it was certain that yellow fever could not "be imported
and spread *without the existence of an atmospheric predisposition to
that disease. . . .*" To the indignation of the anti-quarantine group, the
committee recommended the adoption of quarantine measures, though

it qualified the recommendation by suggesting that the quarantine should restrict commerce as little as possible. To support its position, the majority report of the committee appended a statement from the Chamber of Commerce declaring that a quarantine, rather than hurting business, would be of great benefit to the city.[14] While individual businessmen consistently fought against any restrictions on trade, the more farsighted ones recognized the danger to the city's growth if it should be looked upon as a focal point for yellow fever and other epidemic diseases. They may not have been familiar with the word, but they were concerned with the city's "image!"

The minority group of the committee, in its report, denounced the proposed quarantine as useless to public health and harmful to business. In its place, the group proposed an extensive program of sanitary reform, including among other recommendations improved housing for the poor.[15] Meanwhile the Sanitary Commission had concluded its labors and reported its findings in a 542-page book. Dr. Barton, chairman of the commission and author of much of the report, strongly advocated a comprehensive sanitary program for the city, blaming yellow fever largely on the omnipresent filth and dirt. Accepting Dr. Rush's concept of the unity of fevers, he argued that whenever a combination of certain atmospheric conditions and putrefying filth occurred, various remittent, intermittent, nervous, and other types of fever developed. Under certain conditions, these fevers tended to merge into a pestilential or yellow fever. The only solution for the yellow fever problem was to maintain a high degree of municipal sanitation. He then proposed a whole sanitary program, including improved sewage and water systems, control of food supplies, and the strict regulation of buildings and tenements.

Although the tenor of the report stressed the role of environmental conditions in bringing on yellow fever—and by implication supported the thesis that yellow fever was spontaneously generated in dirt and filth —the Sanitary Commission firmly recommended a system of quarantine. The publication of the legislative and Sanitary Commission reports outraged the anti-quarantine faction, and open warfare immediately broke out in print. The *Picayune* greeted the report of the legislative committee with great joy, noting that support by the Chamber of Commerce for a quarantine removed the only plausible objection to it. On March 9 the editor wrote that "with the almost unanimous opinion of the people of New Orleans, and we believe, also, of the whole State . . . on the side of quarantine, we can hardly conceive it possible that our Legislature should be so forgetful of its obligations as to adjourn without making careful and adequate provision on this important subject." [16] The legislature, however, reluctant to commit itself while the quarantine arguments still raged, voted by a large majority to postpone all resolutions, reports, and bills pertaining to quarantine laws until the next year's session.

Thus, by the spring of 1854, six months after New Orleans had suffered the most disastrous epidemic in its long history, after dozens of petitions and resolutions had been presented to the City Council and to the legislature, after hundreds of pages of arguments and discussions on the subject of sanitary regulations and quarantine, and after bitter debates within the medical societies, nothing had been accomplished. The city fathers had discussed and debated the need for a board of health and quarantine measures until the subject, worn thin by handling, died a natural death; and the health measures only avoided a similar fate in the state legislature by a tabling of the issue for another year. "There seems to be an inexplicable indifference," one of the newspapers stated, "on the part of our public authorities relative to the public health." Ask them to adopt sanitary measures, and they talk of the importance and necessity of quarantine. Urge them to establish a quarantine, and they cry about "the destruction of our commerce, &c., &c., and harp upon the urgency of local measures." [17]

The *New Orleans Medical & Surgical Journal*, under the editorship of Dr. Fenner, denounced the deplorable condition of the streets and the lack of a board of health and predicted that nothing would be done until the appearance of another epidemic, when "our Aldermanic sages will again be roused from their lethargy and spend large sums of money in vain efforts to stay its progress." The councilmen were now looking to quarantine measures to solve their problems, he wrote, but if they would see the dirt and filth everywhere around them, they would realize that the danger lay much closer at hand.[18] A resident of New Orleans, Thomas K. Wharton, commented in his diary on April 25 that almost two thousand immigrants had landed in the city during the past few days, and he wondered what would happen to them in the coming summer "with no Quarantine laws—no sanitary arrangements worth a straw—a feeble city government, an inefficient police, and an embarrassed city finance. The Lord help the unacclimated stranger, and the citizen too, whom business ties here for the summer." [19]

With the onset of warm weather, the City Council again manfully turned its attention to establishing a board of health. Once more an elaborate sanitary program was proposed, and once again the newspapers rejoiced to see the councilmen coming to grips with the issue, but the results were the same. If the assistant aldermen agreed on some provision, the aldermen opposed it, and vice versa. At meeting after meeting the question was debated until July 18, when the aldermen discovered they did not have a quorum and quietly adjourned until the first Tuesday in October.[20] Their decision was undoubtedly influenced by the return of yellow fever on a major epidemic scale. Despite a drastic reduction in the number of nonimmunes, almost twenty-five hundred died in the summer and fall of 1854. Although the outbreak was considered serious by many people, wrote Thomas Wharton, "yet coming after the frightful pestilence of last summer it seems to excite but little attention." Illustrating both the violence of the epidemic and the unconcern of the citizens, he remarked that "the victims of the epidemic are still immense judging from the white and black crepe hanging from the doors of dwelling houses, and the closed stores and the white printed notices fluttering from the lamp posts at the street corner, still the city in general looks cheerful and busy. . . ."[21]

The agitation for action to prevent the recurrence of yellow fever created a tremendous intellectual ferment within the medical profession. While the newspapers often expressed doubts about specific proposals but were willing to give them a trial, the most outspoken physicians, who often represented exceedingly diverse viewpoints, were too convinced of the validity of their own theories to make any concessions. In letters to the newspapers, in pamphlets, and in the medical journals they firmly set forth their own ideas, denounced the opposing views of their colleagues, and, occasionally, as the arguments waxed bitter, launched caustic personal attacks upon their intellectual opponents.

One of the first medical men to write publicly on the 1853 epidemic was Dr. J. S. McFarlane, who addressed a series of letters to the *Delta* in the early days of August. In his first letter he agreed that heat, moisture, vegetable decomposition, and so forth were responsible for precipitating disease, but he denied that they had any effect upon yellow fever. Expressing a traditional medical belief, he asserted: "The influence of one poison counteracting the effects of another is not only the very sheet-anchor of medical practice but is familiar to every mind." Empirically, physicians had learned that poisonous drugs such as mercury and arsenicals were effective in treating certain diseases; hence the assumption that poisons counteract each other. McFarlane then argued that yellow fever was a separate and distinct disease from the intermittent and remittent fevers. This being the case, "every agent which is known to produce other diseases, such as heat, filth, moisture, and vegetable decomposition, must be, to a certain extent, calculated to qualify and neutralize the peculiar and specific atmospheric cause on which yellow fever depends, and thus retard, control, mitigate, or prevent it."

In his second letter Dr. McFarlane expounded further on the subject. He pointed out that in New York and other cities yellow fever struck only in certain years. Since dirt and filth were to be found every year, he asked, why was it that the disease appeared only occasionally.[22] The New Orleans newspapers greeted McFarlane's thesis with derision. The *Crescent* declared that according to McFarlane, the street commissioner had conferred a favor upon New Orleans by failing to perform his duties. His theory, the editor went on, should prove of immeasurable benefit to public finances, since it would save the cost of removing dirt and filth, and of scattering thousands of barrels of lime. The editor then suggested satirically that the health authorities spend more money on poisoned sausages in order to prevent yellow fever by scattering the streets with the bloated carcasses of dead dogs. The whole idea was ridiculous, he concluded, for it is a well-known fact that those living in the dirtiest sections of town are always the most vulnerable to the disease. "Indeed," he gibed, "if filth be a protection, then New Orleans ought to be the healthiest city in the world!" [23]

McFarlane's response was another long letter. After all, he said, refined and dainty young ladies go to various health springs to imbibe 'sulphuretted hydroged gas' for their health. And the fact that poisons tend to counteract each other, he declared, was clearly illustrated during the New Orleans yellow fever epidemic of 1832. Cases of Asiatic cholera had suddenly appeared and within three days "not a single case of yellow fever existed in the whole city." The editors remained unconvinced, and the exchanges between McFarlane and the newspapers continued for some days, despite the fact that residents of New Orleans at this time were dying at the rate of 150 to 200 per day. The *Commercial Bulletin* best summed up the attitude of the daily journals when it declared editorially: "We venture to say, that in no other civilized city in the world, has such an absurd and outrageous theory ever been advanced to justify or extenuate municipal derelection." [24]

The novelty of McFarlane's idea gave it wide publicity in American medical journals and magazines, and the reactions usually ranged from shock and amazement to derision and amusement. Despite the apparent ridiculousness of his viewpoint, McFarlane's letters were generally couched in reasonable terms—far more so than the writings of his critics —and he did have a good point. Yellow fever is a specific disease entity and is not spontaneously generated in dirt and filth. Even his contemporaries had to admit that the disease did occur in cities and towns located on dry, high ground and in which sanitary arrangements were more than adequate. Moreover, if dirt and filth were the only prerequisites for yellow fever, virtually every major city in the United States in the 1850's would have been devastated by this pestilence. McFarlane's observations were correct, but unfortunately his logic was no better than that of his critics.

After the epidemic was over, McFarlane blamed the outbreaks of yellow fever upon the attempts by the authorities to drain the swamps back of the city. The water covering the filth protected it from the sun's rays, he declared, thereby preventing miasma and resultant disease. Quarantine, he thought, was absolutely useless. It had been tried in New Orleans, Natchez, and Galveston without any success, but he despaired of convincing the quarantine advocates of this self-evident truth: "With such men it is useless to argue; reasoning cannot enlighten them nor demonstration convince them." As for yellow fever, he was convinced that neither sanitary measures nor quarantine would have any effect. Eventually, he said, it would wear itself out and disappear from New Orleans, "as it has done under similar circumstances in so many other cities." [25]

Dr. E. D. Fenner, one of the city's outstanding physicians, disagreed with McFarlane on sanitation but saw eye to eye with him on the issue of quarantine. Several years earlier, in an address before the American Medical Association, Fenner had referred to the thesis that yellow fever was imported into New Orleans from the West Indies as "that *old delusion*." As for quarantine, he declared at that time, it had been tried and had "signally failed." In 1854 Dr. Fenner was still convinced that the disease was a product of putrefying filth and atmospheric conditions. He argued that if the disease were imported, it should have occurred every year instead of about every three years. He was willing to try quarantine measures again, even though he was doubtful of their efficacy, "provided the *more rational and hopeful measures of protection be not neglected*. I mean," he explained, "such measures as belong to a strict and efficient sanitary police for the whole city." In answer to those who objected to the cost of a thorough sanitation program, he asked: "Is it not better to spend many thousands of dollars annually for the *preservation* of our people, than millions, as we do for attending them during *sickness, and burying them when dead?*" He would not guarantee that the adoption of his proposals would put an end to yellow fever, but he was sure that purifying and cleansing the city would greatly reduce both the number and virulence of the epidemics.[26]

The calm and fairly reasonable attitude manifested by McFarlane and Fenner was not evident in the writings of Dr. M. Morton Dowler. Dowler launched a sharp attack on Dr. Edward Barton, chairman of the Sanitary Commission, but whether the caustic exchanges reflected a personality clash or were the result of sharp differences of opinion is difficult to say. In his report for the Sanitary Commission, Barton had recommended the expenditure of $1,435,000 to drain, sewer, and provide a sound sanitary organization for New Orleans. While the figure was enormous for its day, Fenner and the other advocates of sanitation argued that, even aside from the human cost of epidemics, this amount was not large in relation to the economic cost of the recurrent pestilences. Dr. Dowler was outraged at the proposal, feeling that such exorbitant expenditures would surely ruin the city. When Barton requested public funds to publish the Sanitary Commission report, Dowler was even more shocked. While he commended the work of the other members of the commission, he declared of Barton that it was his intention "to lay the public purse under contribution for the publication of what he unwarrantably denominates *a Report*, but which is really a tedious book, abounding in absurdities, extravagances, and self-glorification, totally unexampled in the annals of official documents of our science." Leaving no doubt as to his view of Dr. Barton, he wrote: "The truth is, Dr. Barton has long been, mentally speaking, in an *interesting condition*, and having excellent reasons to distrust the natural efforts of book-birth, he has deemed it proper to have recourse to the municipal forceps, and the delivery has thus been greatly facilitated." [27]

Dr. Dowler was equally convinced that quarantine was as useless against yellow fever as sanitary measures. In fact, he really saw no need for doing anything. Writing in July of 1854, when the city was suffering from its second consecutive yellow fever epidemic, he asserted: "I am far from considering New Orleans an unhealthy city, so far as her resident and native population is concerned." He decried the fallacies "promulgated by those who have attempted to write down the reputation of the city with regard to salubrity," and hoped that the city government would never again "organize another of those useless debating societies called a 'Board of Health.'" He dismissed McFarlane's thesis that yellow fever was a specific disease, but he was equally scornful of those who believed the disorder arose from corruption and dirt. Regardless of what efforts were made, he concluded, because of the "inexorable law of accumulative mortality," the ever-present fevers could be expected to flare up periodically into a pestilential form.[28]

While Dr. McFarlane's theory brought shocked outcries from the New Orleans newspapers, those of Dr. Samuel A. Cartwright, which were much farther afield, were viewed with considerable respect. In the summer of 1854 Dr. Cartwright wrote a long article entitled "On the Prevention of Yellow Fever" in which he explained the physiological basis for yellow fever. The wealthy classes in New Orleans tended to construct their homes and buildings largely during the summer months, he stated, causing immigrant workers to be employed in the broiling sun. At the same time, the city authorities, during their annual cleanup campaigns, put other armies of impoverished immigrants to work "pulling and hauling the filthy mud of the gutters," thus filling the city "with clouds of miasmatic vapors." All of these immigrants, exposed to the sun while performing laborious drudgery, "were breathing an atmosphere much more rarified than that which they had been accustomed to in their native country." Consequently they did not obtain sufficient oxygen, their lungs did not function properly, and carbonic acid and other wastes were not eliminated from the blood. While moderate labor in a cool climate was healthful, "hard labor in the hot sun causes a rapid degeneration of the tissues within the body of the white man. . . ." On the other hand, the Negro, because "of his enormous liver and by the peculiar construction of the skin," was easily able to throw off all waste substances. "This physiological fact," Dr. Cartwright asserted, could not be denied.

Having laid a firm scientific basis, Dr. Cartwright then proceeded to the solution. He began by warning his readers that all sanitary measures are ineffectual "unless the practice of making negroes out of the master race of men, and turning them out to labor in the hot summer's sun, be abolished." Once this thesis was accepted, the first step should be to construct buildings and sidewalks so as to provide ample shade, since "exposure to the sun is both a predisposing and an exciting cause of yellow fever." Next he recommended improving privies and introducing ample supplies of fresh pure water into the city. A third step was to insist that all doors and windows of the sickroom be thrown wide open, for "yellow fever is never communicated in a room properly ventilated." Finally, he wrote, there is an immutable law which says that "the aristocracy of the white skin . . . shall not be hewers of wood or drawers of water, or wallow in the sloughs of intemperance, under pain of three fourths of their number being cut-off." It was the immigrant laborers who, by disregarding nature's law, had led "the world into the error that New Orleans is a most sickly location. . . . The truth is," he declared, "there is no city in the Union more favorable to health and longevity."

On the subject of quarantine, he was emphatic in his opposition; it had been tried before and in every case had been found wanting. There was, however, a short, cheap, and safe way to prevent the introduction of yellow fever from abroad, "admitting, for the sake of argument, that it can be introduced in that way and spread to the inhabitants. . . . It is simply to insulate the shipping with well acclimated negroes, and to let no other class of people act as stevedores, or to come within a specified distance of the wharf—precisely as smallpox is insulated by those who have had the disease in the natural way. Negroes are perfect non-conductors of yellow fever." This method would not only prove far more effective than any other, but it "would have the merit of involving no expense, and of throwing no obstruction in the way of commerce." [29]

In August a letter to the *Weekly Delta* signed "Tuckahoe," but which sounds suspiciously like Dr. Cartwright, argued that yellow fever proved that slavery was a blessing to the Negroes. The writer pointed out that nearly all yellow fever victims were white laborers, while Negro slaves and white slaveholders remained exempt from the disorder. Two months later the editor of the *Daily Delta*, commenting upon an article in a northern newspaper which attempted to show that yellow fever was a consequence of slavery, proved to his own satisfaction that slavery was actually beneficial. Negroes in New Orleans, declared the editors, are exempt from the fever except for those who go north and then return, and nearly all Negroes who die of yellow fever are freemen. "To the superstitious," the editor commented piously, "it would seem that God intended to mark with his punishment and frown upon any attempt of the negro to exist in climates and regions, which are adapted to the organization of the white man." The Negro could only live in these regions, the editor concluded, where the beneficent effect of slavery "exempts him from a destructive disease, to which he would render himself liable by the exercise of his freedom." [30]

By the 1850's slavery as an institution was outmoded in the western world, and the South found its peculiar institution coming under greater and greater attack. Instinctively the South began closing ranks, and members of all professions put their special knowledge and talent to the service of what has been called southern nationalism. Just as southern theologians found justification for slavery in Christianity, so the medical profession attempted to prove on the basis of anatomical and physiological knowledge that Negroes were both different and inferior to the whites. It was argued that climatic conditions and the existence of large groups of Negroes made southern medical practice quite different from that of Europe and the North. The logical conclusion was that southerners should be educated in southern medical schools. In the light of this background, it is not surprising that Dr. Cartwright's ideas, which were based on the innate differences between the two races, should have been given serious consideration. Surprisingly, a buffer of immune Negroes conceivably could have worked had it been possible to make the buffer zone wide enough to compensate for the flight of the mosquito and if the crews and passengers had been prevented from freely passing through. Without a knowledge of the role of the mosquito, however, no quarantine system could have been very effective, and, in any case, Dr. Cartwright's theory was never given a trial.

Public indignation with the state legislature and the City Council over their failure to enact health measures after the 1853 epidemic was high enough, but the second major epidemic in the summer of 1854 proved the final straw. When the legislature met early in 1855, the issue could no longer be evaded. By this time, too, although the quarantine debate continued, public opinion had generally crystallized in favor of restricting trade with the yellow fever areas. On March 15, 1855, "An Act to Establish Quarantine for the Protection of the State" was placed on the statute books. It provided for a fairly effective quarantine system and set up the first permanent state board of health in the United States. The board was to consist of nine members, six appointed by the governor and three by the New Orleans City Council. To guarantee that the health board members did not nullify the intent of the legislature, the law provided that "the said members shall be selected in reference to their known zeal in favor of a quarantine system." [31]

This State Board of Health, which during its early years was concerned primarily with enforcing quarantine regulations and the affairs of New Orleans, immediately ran into a storm of opposition. Its early history was a tumultuous one, but it did manage to survive, and succeeding years saw its powers gradually extended. Although the indirect effects of the yellow fever epidemic of 1853 were to linger for many years, the creation of the State Board of Health marked the end of the direct results of the tragic summer of 1853.

CHAPTER X

Physicians and Fevers

Wɪᴛʜ ᴛʜᴇ ʙᴀᴄᴛᴇʀɪᴏʟᴏɢɪᴄᴀʟ ᴇxᴘʟᴀɴᴀᴛɪᴏɴ of communicable diseases still in the future, the medical profession was unable to determine the origin and causative factors for most diseases. In the case of malaria, the miasmatic thesis provided both a logical explanation for the disease and a practical means of preventing it. Since the miasma arose only from damp, swampy land, one could avoid malaria by shunning such areas or could remove the cause by draining the land. Smallpox was a horrible disease, unquestionably contagious, but it could be prevented by means of vaccination. Precisely how vaccination worked was not known, but its success was obvious to all but a few diehards in the medical profession. Parenthetically it can be observed that the antivaccination movement was as vocal—and far more logical—in the late nineteenth century as the antifluoridation groups are today.

The large group of ailments which our forebears lumped under the heading of fevers or "eruptive" fevers still presented to them an unsolvable problem. The clinical symptoms of typhus, typhoid, and scarlet fever, for example, had been clearly differentiated; but the nature of the diseases was a complete puzzle. Were these disorders separate entities or were they merely different forms of one basic fever? Was the form which the fever assumed dependent upon the individual's constitution? For example, would fever assume the form of typhus in one person and typhoid in another? Were the particular symptoms of fever determined by atmospheric conditions or other meteorological factors; or were environmental conditions such as dirt, crowding, and dampness of significance? What was the role of personal or moral qualities? Certainly the temperate, prudent, moderate, and industrious seemed to be more resistant than the intemperate and dissolute. Why was it that new-comers to any area were more susceptible to the prevailing diseases than natives or those who had resided there for some years?

Every question which applied to the other epidemic diseases seemed even more unanswerable in the case of yellow fever. Almost in despair, Dr. Axson, editor of the *New Orleans Monthly Medical Register*, asked in September of 1853: "Why is it that in '52, on the same soil, among the same population, under the same climatic influences, the same disease, felt in its most benign forms and scarcely attracting notice among the current events of the passing hour, becomes in '53, a deadly pestilence, scattering death, dismay and suffering among our affrighted popula-tion?" [1] In reply to the standard argument of the sanitationists—that yellow fever was a product of crowding, filth, dampness, and the ex-halations from putrefying vegetable and animal matter—the *Delta* on September 1 discussed the extensive sanitary program which the city of Mobile had undertaken to keep yellow fever at bay. "And yet in clean, salubrious Mobile, on a dry shell bank, with the breezes from the sea to blow through her streets, this disease prevails as violently as in our swamp-girt, filthy, badly-governed city! Where now is the theory which locates the 'origin' of the fever in the gutters and swamp?" Fur-ther emphasizing his point the editor wrote: "Alas! where is Natchez?—poor, desolated, abandoned, stricken Natchez!—perched on a lofty bluff, dry, salubrious and healthy!" [2]

Throughout every yellow fever epidemic, the citizens of New Or-leans had looked forward eagerly to the onset of cool weather and frosts, knowing that the disease was sure to subside. A correspondent to one of the New Orleans newspapers early in September argued that yellow fever must be an imported disease since it is "an exotic" where-ever ice and frost occur. A few days later the *Bee* pointed out that the cool weather theory had little applicability to the present epidemic since the weather was unusually hot this September, yet the number of cases was sharply declining.[3] Dr. Abner Hester editorialized on this same theme in the November issue of the *New Orleans Medical & Surgical Journal*. It would appear, he wrote, "that the popular and oft-expressed belief, that a frost was absolutely required to put a period to—to arrest and extinguish the epidemic, has been falsified by the events of this season." The epidemic has ended, and yet "there has been no frost—no freeze—and only a few days of cool, north wind." He doubted that the evidence would convince many people, since "the conviction that a frost is requisite to destroy the yellow fever is so firmly fixed in the popular, no less than the professional mind, that we fear no array of facts nor progress of reasoning can divert it from this long established belief." [4]

The 1853 epidemic, Dr. Hester continued, showed many dissimilarities from its predecessors. It had proved more fatal and had run its course more rapidly. Its victims had experienced more head and stomach symptoms and less kidney problems than in previous outbreaks. Moreover, patients had not responded so favorably to large doses of quinine as had been the case earlier. Another unique feature of the present epidemic was that it had "the power to propagate itself from one subject to another. In a word it seemed to be *infectious.* . . ." If one can assume "the constitution of the atmosphere to be the same for the two seasons [1847 and 1853]," then the "poison of the disease, the *materies morbi*" must have been more active or more virulent in 1853, or else it was a separate and distinct disease from that which prevailed in 1847. [5]

Although the "constitution of the atmosphere certainly favored the transmission of the poison, from one point to another," Dr. Hester wrote, "we have other facts to prove, that in several instances, the fever perished with those who conveyed it to particular localities." At the same time, he said, it appeared in some communities which had no connection with either diseased persons or infected localities. "Thus, we have evidence both *for* and *against* the transmissibility and infectiousness of the disease." The questions which Dr. Hester raised had been anticipated by one of the local newspapers in September. Its editor asked how does yellow fever spread if it is not imported and is not spread by contagion? Equally baffled by this seemingly unanswerable puzzle, he concluded: "Certainly science and philanthropy never had a wider field of investigation and labor, than is presented in the inquiry into the causes and nature of this terrible malady." [6]

The medical profession may not have known the cause of yellow fever, but few of its members had any doubts as to their ability to treat its victims. Confronted with sick and dying patients, the doctors could scarcely stand by calmly and objectively viewing the suffering. Patients expected the doctors to do something, and the majority of physicians were not inclined to disappoint those expectations. Most were men of action who preferred to battle the disease—if necessary, to the death! In the 1850's many southern physicians, like their counterparts in the North, still had only a limited amount of medical training. One year's apprenticeship in a doctor's office and a course of lectures lasting from ten to sixteen weeks was the basic requirement for a degree in most medical schools. A number of schools required their students to attend two years of lectures, but since the course of lectures was the same for both years, this requirement had only a limited value. Moreover, America's burgeoning population had created a great demand for surgeons and physicians, and one result had been a spawning of proprietary medical schools in the years from 1820 to 1850. Many of these were little more than diploma mills, and even among the legitimate schools, a large portion had neither an adequate faculty nor clinical facilities.[7]

New Orleans, as the leading southwestern medical center, was fortunate—or unfortunate, depending upon one's view of the medical theories of the day—in having a first-rate medical school, the Medical College of the University of Louisiana, and two good medical journals. In addition to the products of its own medical school, physicians and surgeons from Great Britain and the Continent were often attracted to this major port city. Moreover, the Creoles, the proud descendants of the original French settlers, scorned what they felt to be the crude empiricism of American medicine and sent their sons to France for professional training. Thus, New Orleans was well represented by two quite divergent schools of medicine.

Even the most empirical physicians are inevitably influenced by the prevailing concepts, and the one which was probably most basic in the mid-nineteenth century was the humoral theory. This theory, borrowed from the Greeks and modified by the Roman physician, Galen, profoundly affected Western medical thought and is still reflected in our language by such terms as good and ill humor. Briefly, it postulated that the body contained four humors and that illness was a result of an imbalance of these four substances. A plethora or excess of humors was to be treated by depletion—bleeding, blistering, purging, vomiting, and sweating—whereas a deficiency required that the patient be given stimulants and a supportive diet. A variation of the humoral thesis was the idea that the introduction of "morbific" or "peccant" (poisonous) substances could corrupt the blood and other humors and thus bring on illness. Here, too, the aim of the treatment was to rid the body of these bad humors, and depletion was the standard procedure.[8]

Among the new concepts which developed in the eighteenth century, one attributed disease either to tension or to the extreme relaxation of the nervous and vascular systems. Sickness, then, was caused by the muscles and nervous system responding too violently or too inadequately to internal or external stimuli. In terms of American medical practice, a variation of this thesis set forth by Dr. Benjamin Rush was of profound significance. Dr. Rush believed in the "unity of fevers," a concept which held that all sickness was merely one aspect of fever and that fever was the product of capillary tension. He had noted that "a spasm of the extreme arteries" or capillaries was a concomitant of fever and assumed the spasm to be the cause. Emotions or an individual's mental state could provide an internal stimulus, and miasma, for example, could supply an external stimulus. As a medical theorist, Dr. Rush was only one of many in an age of speculation; but it was in the area of medical practice—in which he relied upon bloodletting and purging to a horrifying degree—that he made his greatest impact upon American medicine.

Rush felt that the chief purpose of the blood was to stimulate the action of the heart and arteries, "thereby imparting extensive and uniform impressions to every animal fibre." He said it had been observed "that in those persons who die of hunger, there is no diminution of the quantity of blood in the large blood vessels." If the patient was overstimulated, and if the blood's chief function was to stimulate, then it was logical to reduce the amount of blood. So sure was Rush of his theory that he advocated removing as much as four-fifths of a patient's blood in desperate cases! Bloodletting had been a traditional therapeutic, but Dr. Rush and some of his European contemporaries inaugurated an unprecedented era of depletion. In the South and West, where Dr. Rush's influence lasted well past mid-century, physicians were long noted for the strenuousness of their practice.[9]

Bleeding was only one aspect of medical treatment. Vomiting and purging to cleanse the system were fundamental to the cure of any and all disorders. Indeed, a physician who failed to prescribe a horrendous dose of calomel, gamboge, castor oil, or any of the other standard purgatives of this rigorous age would be considered remiss by both his patients and his colleagues. Blistering, another traditional medical technique, eminently suited the prevailing notions about therapy. For centuries patients had been conditioned to rigorous treatment, and they expected the therapy to be painful and unpleasant. Thus the more nauseating a medicine tasted, or the more painful a remedy felt, the more efficacious it was assumed to be. Blistering consisted of placing a poultice of some irritating substance on the skin—Spanish fly, or cantharides, was the most common, but a mustard plaster was also effective—until it created the equivalent of a second or third degree burn. It can readily be seen that blistering completely fulfilled the medical requirements of the day. In the first place, it was excruciatingly painful to the patient; in the second place, since the wound was almost certain to become infected and supuration ensue, both the patient and the physician could see in the formation of pus that the blisters were drawing poison from the system.

In addition to various depletory techniques, southern physicians in the first half of the nineteenth century had a wide range of botanical and mineral pharmaceuticals to draw upon, and most of these were administered with an unsparing hand. The two medicines basic to any treatment in the South were calomel and quinine. Calomel, or mercurous chloride, in reasonable doses acts as a laxative, but it is a dangerous drug under the best of circumstances. Considering the cavalier fashion in which it was prescribed in the nineteenth century, it must have caused incalculable damage. An excessive dosage can bring on acute mercurial poisoning, the first symptoms of which are enlargement of the salivary glands and an excessive flow of saliva. Soon the breath becomes fetid, the gums and tongue ulcerated, and eventually the teeth may fall out. Over and above these more obvious symptoms, serious general neurological complications may ensue. Yet a standard prescription of early physicians was to take calomel until "salivation." The patient was not considered to be deriving any real benefit from his medicine until he was showing the first evidence of acute mercurial poisoning!

Louisiana was more fortunate than other southern states because of the presence of a large French population. Since the Creoles tended to hold themselves aloof from the crude, boisterous Anglo-Saxons who poured into Louisiana in the years following the Louisiana Purchase, two cultural groups developed side by side. French physicians in Louisiana, who were highly dubious of the heroic medicines of their English-speaking counterparts, generally practiced in a more moderate fashion, leaving much of the cure to nature.

The French Revolution and the Napoleonic Era had reorganized French medicine and created a favorable milieu for clinical research, thereby enabling France to take leadership in the field of medicine during the first half of the nineteenth century. A combination of circumstances led French doctors on the path to a more objective and scientific approach, one aspect of which was correlating clinical findings with those of the pathologist. For the first time, large numbers of patients were systematically examined, treated, and, when necessary, followed to the death house. Not only did it become possible to classify their disorders and symptoms more accurately, but it was also possible to determine the value of particular forms of therapy. It soon became apparent that the patient's recovery or death often bore little relationship to the therapy prescribed or the drugs administered. French clinicians consequently became so skeptical about the use of drugs that their attitude verged on therapeutic nihilism. Hence, the young Louisiana Creoles who were sent to France for their medical training returned even more convinced of the value of leaving the patient alone and permitting nature to work the cure.

In the years prior to the great epidemic of 1853 the treatment accorded yellow fever patients in Louisiana showed the wide divergence between the Creole and American schools of medicine. In reporting on one of the early outbreaks to the *Société Médicale de la Nouvelle-Orléans*, the medical organization of the French-speaking physicians, Dr. A. A. Gros and Dr. N. V. A. Gerardin wrote: "Experience had proved that in the violence of the epidemic, bleeding and vomiting were generally harmful." The two doctors objected to the practice of some of their American colleagues of pouring cold water over fever patients and recommended instead that they be given tepid baths. The best way to promote recovery, they asserted, was through good nursing and the use of "gentle evacuants, acid drinks with cream of tartar, tamerind, orange juice and lemon juice; whey, emollient clysters and purgatives." [10]

The American physicians had nothing but contempt for what they termed the timidity of the French. One of them declared of yellow fever that he had never "witnessed a single instance of mortality wherein it [bleeding and purging] was employed during the precursory symptoms." Another Louisiana doctor, M. L. Haynie, wrote that the Creole physicians were "extremely averse to using mercury in any form; and generally, as much opposed to the use of the lancet; from an idea, I presume, that the mercury never can be eradicated from the system, and that the quantity of blood is already too small, or could not be supplied if any was taken away; an error founded on a want of correct physiological knowledge." Confident of his own understanding of physiology, Dr. Haynie recommended immediate bleeding "to ease the heart and arteries." Since prostration was always present in yellow fever, he declared, stimulants were "the only anchor of hope; and mercury affords one, the most *uniform and immediate* in its effect, as well as the most lasting." Clearly illustrating the full implications of the term "heroic medicine," he added, "A few hundred grains (the quantity is not dangerous) introduced into the system, will excite a pulse *fuller*, *stronger*, and more *durable* than any other stimulus, I have ever used in similar cases."

A phrase found in one of the southern medical journals, "desperate diseases require desperate remedies," typifies the attitude of many southern physicians. Dr. Haynie, for example, clearly expressed this idea when he stated that he proportioned his dosages of calomel according to the violence of the disease, usually giving from one to two hundred grains an hour! "It is but trifling with the life of a man, to give him less of a remedy than his disease calls for." [11] Fortunately, as the nineteenth century advanced, a swelling chorus of opposition to the excessive use of calomel and bloodletting sounded throughout the country. The public attitude was reflected in the chorus of a popular song:

> And when I must resign my breath,
> Pray let me die a natural death
> And bid the world a fond farewell,
> Without one dose of calomel!

As public suspicion with respect to the medical profession increased, a number of irregular medical groups appeared: hydropaths, who advocated cold showers, moderate diet, and exercise; Thomsonians, who relied solely upon botanicals; and homeopaths, whose theories were even more elaborate and esoteric than those of the regular profession, but whose virtue lay in a medical practice which almost eliminated the use of drugs. The homeopaths believed that the smaller the amount of the prescription, the greater would be its benefit. And patients treated by these doctors who let nature take its course survived far better than those who were bled, blistered, and dosed with calomel, quinine, and the other weapons in the regular physicians' armamentarium.

As a reaction set in against the excessive use of calomel in the 1830's and 1840's, quinine emerged as the leading southern "anti-fevrum." The success of Peruvian or cinchona bark—only two of its many names—in the treatment of malaria had led to its general prescription for any and all fevers. In 1820 the alkaloid quinine was isolated from cinchona bark and quickly replaced the use of the bark itself. Although quinine is effective in reducing fever and is a specific—probably the best one in existence—for malaria, it had little value in treating yellow fever, typhoid, typhus, and all the other disorders lumped under the rubric of "fever" during these years. It had, moreover, serious side-effects, and could be quite dangerous when given in large enough doses. Nonetheless, in the 1840's the practice of treating yellow fever with large doses of quinine became quite popular. One group, which followed what was called "the quinine practice," combined this treatment with bleeding to unconsciousness. The physician on first seeing the patient would open a vein with his lancet and let the blood flow until the patient fainted. When the patient was revived, he would be given 15 or more grains of quinine and ordered to take additional doses at various intervals. Although calomel was losing its status among New Orleans physicians by 1853, quinine and bleeding were still considered prime weapons in the fight against yellow fever.

By 1853 the antipathy between the English and French physicians in Louisiana was gradually dying down, and the more moderate physicians in both groups were beginning to recognize the better aspects of their respective practices. Laymen, however, were still dubious of the medical profession, and their suspicions were not lightened by the bitter and public quarrels within the ranks of the physicians. The vitriolic debates in local medical societies frequently erupted into pamphlet warfare and open denunciations in the newspapers. What would begin as an intellectual clash between the proponents of opposing medical theories occasionally ended in fisticuffs, public brawls, and even duels. With the doctors denouncing one another's theories and practices, it was small wonder that the public sought for medical help outside the profession and that outright quacks and aberrant medical cults flourished like the Green Bay Tree.

In the summer of 1853 the editorials and items in the New Orleans newspapers clearly show the public distrust of its doctors. In August Dr. J. Lightcap inserted a notice in the *Crescent* stating that he had visited the family of Captain James Price on the corner of Hevia and Baronne streets merely as a friend of the family. He had not prescribed for any of them, and, he added significantly, "I had nothing to do with their treatment." A few days later a correspondent who signed himself "A. C. J." ascribed the excessive death toll from yellow fever to the presence of too many doctors, whom he defined as "parchment M.D.'s who are licensed to kill." He cited the case of three young men who had been pronounced incurable by a certain physician. A member of the Howard Association who refused to accept this prognosis had nursed the men back to convalescence, when another doctor who chanced to be in the neighborhood "forced [the patients] to take medicine which he prescribed, and in less than twelve hours after, '*all were dead.*' "

The correspondent disclaimed any hostility to the profession since

PHYSICIANS AND FEVERS 155

many of its members, he said, were skillful and humane. But, he continued, "while it is the fashion to make the 'fool of the family' a student of medicine, and the many rival medical colleges grant diplomas to all who pay for the course of lectures, it is time now, when death stalks us, to draw a distinction and prevent very many of those miscalled doctors from approaching the sick." Another correspondent subsequently denied the charges, and a bitter written exchange took place.[12]

A more reasonable complaint was voiced in the *Delta* in a letter from "E.J.C." This writer told of an eleven-year-old boy who had awakened in the night with a slight fever. His parents gave him a moderate dose of castor oil, whereupon he fell asleep and awoke in the morning perspiring freely and with only a slight headache. At 8:30 A.M. a doctor passed by and was asked to see the boy. He examined the child, declared he was doing well, and ordered that he be given thirty grains of quinine and five grains of opium compounded into ten pills, two of which were to be given every four hours. Within an hour after taking the first two pills, the boy lapsed into unconsciousness and died a few hours later. In a reasonable manner, the writer asked whether the medicine had caused death or whether the boy would have died in any case. His motive in writing to the paper, he asserted, was to request that quinine advocates use judgment and discrimination in prescribing their medicine.[13]

A week or so later a tongue-in-cheek story which purportedly had been heard on the streets appeared in the paper. While two physicians were visiting patients, their Negro carriage drivers were overheard in the following conversation: "Hello, Sam, how many have you killed this morning?" "Times getting might dull, only killed seven & 2 or 3 fast following." "Well, I done killed 14—not a good mornings work. Times getting dull cause so many patients is refusing to take their medicine!" Subsequently a satirical letter from "Observer," who professed to be a doctor, claimed to have found a certain way to reduce temperature in yellow fever cases. As soon as the temperature rose, the patient was to be given ten to fifty grains of quinine and the dose repeated every hour until the fever was broken. This method, declared "Observer," never fails, but he thought that he should mention the almost invariable consequence—the patient seldom survived![14]

Another story to come out of the epidemic told of an old Spaniard who, falling ill with yellow fever, separately summoned three doctors, A., M., and W., and faithfully took the prescriptions of all three. On the fifth day the doctors, by coincidence, all arrived at the patient's bedside about the same time. When W. arrived and found A. examining the patient, he told him he must have made a mistake. A. replied that he had been treating the case for four days and had prescribed one hundred grains of quinine. W. declared that he never administered "that murderous quinine" but had been treating the patient homeopathically since the beginning of his illness. Just at that time M. walked in, glanced at the patient, and declared him to be well. He then informed A. and W. that he had found the patient on the brink of the grave, but by repeated bleeding and administering a strong emetic and forty grains of calomel he had conquered the yellow fever. A bitter quarrel promptly ensued between the three doctors as to which treatment had provided the cure. As the argument grew heated, the three physicians drew their swords, whereupon the old Spaniard intervened and explained that he had requested the services of all three. The three men angrily stalked off, each convinced that he had cured the patient.[15]

The editors of the local newspapers occasionally inveighed against what they felt was irresponsible medical practice. An editorial early in September praised the work of some physicians but declared that upstarts and newcomers to the profession had "nearly emptied the apothecaries' shops of various poisonous drugs . . . and had filled many graves that might otherwise not have been dug." Assertions are heard repeatedly, the editorial continued, that physicians have been directly responsible for the deaths of their patients. Whether this is true, the conflicts of opinion within the medical profession create "a most alarming uncertainty" with respect to the practice in this city.[16]

One of the Howard Association members, William L. Robinson, whose work during the many yellow fever epidemics brought him in close contact with the physicians, became quite skeptical about the profession. "To listen to one physician expatiating upon the charming virtues of sulphate of quinine; to hear another pronounce it most poisonous in its uses; one as enthusiastic as the other is denunciatory, and both, in other respects, awarded by their peers the front rank of the profession," he wrote, scarcely engenders respect. "Unity in medicine," he observed cynically, "may as well be looked for as unity in religion: both intend the same result in their contradictions, and it is but charitable to infer that one is as useful to man as the other is acceptable in the eyes of God."[17]

Mr. Robinson's experiences during the epidemic of 1853 would appear to justify his cynicism. He related one instance in which he sent for a physician for two German women whom he found suffering from the fever. The physician arrived, briefly examined the patients, and left a prescription. The medicine was obtained from a pharmacist; but before the patients were able to take it, another doctor arrived, threw the medicine out of the window, and left a different prescription. The two women were doubtful of this latter doctor and refused to take his medicine. Subsequently, the first physician returned, threw out his colleague's drugs, and left still another prescription. Robinson returned to find the patients "in a profuse perspiration, with a healthy pulse," and decided they had no need of drugs. The next morning both physicians arrived together and promptly engaged in a violent quarrel over the treatment until Robinson broke in and suggested they leave. Under Robinson's ministrations, the two patients rapidly recovered without professional help.[18]

Although wide differences of opinion existed even among the regular practitioners as to the best treatment of yellow fever, there was a sincere desire to find the truth. In August the Louisiana State Medical Society established a committee on "Practical Medicine" under the chairmanship of Dr. J. B. M'Kelvey. The committee published a notice in the September New Orleans Medical & Surgical Journal requesting readers to submit in writing their "observations and views, and treatment of yellow fever." In this same issue, Dr. Hester declared it his duty as an editor to bring "before the profession every fact tending to elucidate this peculiar disease." [19]

Hester was among the first to recognize the failure of the quinine practice during the 1853 epidemic. He wrote in August that his experience in this outbreak had convinced him "that large doses of this salt cannot be relied on in the early stages of the attack." While he had used quinine successfully in former yellow fever epidemics, "this season it failed in a majority of cases to sustain its previous high reputation." In a footnote to an article on the use of quinine against yellow fever, he said that the failure of quinine was such that "many of our most respected physicians" have reduced their prescriptions or else stopped using it completely. In response to these comments, Dr. J. C. Batchelor of New Orleans reported that he had found doses of from eight to fifteen grains of quinine to be very efficacious during the early stages of the attack, and that he usually administered from thirty to sixty grains during the first twelve hours. The quinine was given in conjunction "with hot mustard foot bath, diaphoretics, cupping over mastoid or nucha, etc., and later in the epidemic, generally preceding the quinine, with an active emetic of ipecac, lobelia, and sanguinaria . . . and sometimes," he added, "I gave 8 to 12 grains mass hydrarg., with the first dose of quinine." During the early days of the epidemic he had relied upon enemas to keep the bowels open, but later on he "found a free evacuation of the bowels by medicine borne to advantage." The "8 to 12 grains mass hydrarg." he prescribed, was the so-called "blue mass," a standard purgative used widely in the nineteenth century. It consisted of metallic mercury and conserve of roses or liquorice root usually compounded into 3-grain pills. In the case of children, chalk was occasionally added to minimize the rather drastic effect of the medicine. Despite his rigorous treatment, Dr. Batchelor declared that he had lost very few patients when given an opportunity to treat them early in their disease.[20]

Dr. Hester, in commenting upon Dr. Batchelor's letter, reiterated his earlier objections to large doses of quinine and added that "inquiry among some of the best practitioners in this city, has but served to strengthen the suggestion thrown out hastily, on the subject of quinine in yellow fever, in our September No." While not objecting to the use of quinine, he concluded, "we do protest against its indiscriminate administration in such monstrous doses." [21]

Dr. Bennet Dowler, an able New Orleans physician who served as editor of the *New Orleans Medical & Surgical Journal* for a number of years after Dr. Hester's death, was reported by the latter to be prescribing the following for his patients: "Mass Hydrarg., Calomel, Quinine, gr. X, a a., Morphine, gr. ii." These drugs were compounded into ten pills, and the patient was given one every two hours. During the administration of the medicine, he ordered that the patients "be diligently spunged with alcohol and water, until the febrile symptoms subside." According to Hester, Dr. Dowler had found this treatment to be quite successful.[22] The quinine and morphine prescribed by Dowler are self explanatory. The "mass hydrarg." was a purgative; and the calomel, or mercurous chloride, was used as an alterative, a medicine designed to stimulate and promote the health of the tissues. In the light of modern medicine, Dr. Dowler's treatment was rather severe, but at least he omitted the bleeding, blistering, and vomiting recommended by some of his contemporaries, and in terms of his own age his dosage was quite moderate.

The most caustic comment about the excessive use of quinine appeared in an editorial headed "Quinine and Madness," which appeared late in October in the *Delta*. The editor began by declaring that some of the New Orleans newspapers were attributing the increase in madness among recent arrivals in the city "to the reckless use of quinine, which characterized the practice of some physicians during the late epidemic." Quinine, he asserted, "is a subtle poison, and in unskilled or careless hands, becomes as deadly as prussic acid or arsenic." Yet quinine pills were freely administered "by aspiring juveniles—who, by the shamefully ready process which is fashionable amongst us, have obtained the right to place those significant capitals, M.D. after their names—as if they were simple gum-drops or crumbs of bread." The result of this "vigorous practice," he concluded sadly, "can be seen daily, in shattered nervous systems and senses paralyzed." [23]

As large doses of mercury in its various forms began to fall into disrepute, castor oil became for many physicians a favorite cathartic. No one questioned the value of keeping the bowels open—in sickness or in health—and castor oil was effective in so doing. By virtue of its vile taste and violent purgative action, it conformed well with the accepted view of how a medicine should taste and what it should effect. Dr. J. S. McFarlane, a man of real ability but one given to wandering far afield at times, was much opposed to the general use of castor oil. "Never," he wrote, "do I recollect being called to a single case . . . where the patient had not taken a dose of Castor Oil, and rarely did I confer with physicians without being informed that they had commenced the treatment of their cases with a dose of Castor Oil." Because of "the nauseous character of the remedy," patients frequently vomited it, he said; and the dose was then repeated, thus causing "permanent irritability of the stomach" and paving the way for the "black vomit." [24]

In 1854 Dr. Fenner, the leading advocate of quinine in New Orleans, wrote an account of the great epidemic in which he stated: "In New Orleans may be seen the results of every imaginable course of treatment, from *doing nothing at all*, up to the use of *the most potent remedies in heroic doses*; and cases have recovered and died under all. Whilst many have, doubtless, been lost from *want of medical aid*, it cannot be denied that many have likewise died from over-medication. What is to be inferred from this great variety of treatment but that *the true nature and proper management of Yellow Fever are not yet well understood by the mass of those who undertake to treat it*." As for his own treatment, he still felt that quinine, calomel, and bloodletting were of value in the first stages of the disease, but he conceded that once the case was well developed, it was better to rely upon good nursing, minimal medication, and the efforts of nature. Striking back at the mounting public criticism of his profession, he spoke scathingly of those "who have such

HISTORY

OF THE

YELLOW FEVER

NEW ORLEANS,

DURING THE

SUMMER OF 1853.

WITH SKETCHES OF THE

SCENES OF HORROR

WHICH OCCURRED DURING THE EPIDEMIC:

DESCRIPTIONS AND BEAUTIFUL ILLUSTRATIONS OF

CHARITY HOSPITAL, AND THE PUBLIC CEMETERIES,

AND ESPECIALLY OF

POTTER'S FIELD,

AND THE METHOD OF BURYING THE DEAD IN CYPRESS SWAMP.

TO WHICH IS ADDED THE NAMES OF ALL PERSONS WHO CONTRIBUTED TO THE FUNDS OF THE

HOWARD ASSOCIATION,

IN ALL PARTS OF THE UNITED STATES, AND THE AMOUNT CONTRIBUTED BY EACH PERSON,

WITH THE OFFICIAL REPORT

OF THE DOINGS OF THAT SOCIETY, &c.,

BY A PHYSICIAN OF NEW ORLEANS,

WHO WAS PRESENT DURING THE FATAL EPIDEMIC OF 1853.

PHILADELPHIA AND ST. LOUIS,

PUBLISHED BY C. W. KENWORTHY,

1854.

Title page from an account of the epidemic by an anonymous physician. The sketches reproduced in this book are from that pamphlet.

unbounded confidence in the *inherent and unerring wisdom of the People en masse*." He expressed grave apprehensions over the possibility "that the People shall take upon themselves to determine whether quinine or any other medicine shall be given in Yellow Fever or not. . . ." [25]

Dr. McFarlane, after discussing the contradictory symptoms to be found in yellow fever cases, asserted: "Is there then anything surprising in the fact that nothing comprehensive or profitable, in the management of yellow fever, has ever yet been written, and that all the various systems which have from time to time been ushered forth with so much confidence by those who had never seen the disease have regularly exploded, and perished still-born. We are therefore as yet not even at the threshold of science, in our knowledge of the nature and treatment of yellow fever; every effort, so far as proclaimed to the world, has been but the futile struggles of empiricism—a succession of desperate experiments." [26]

Dr. M. Morton Dowler was equally discouraged by the holocaust of yellow fever which had consumed so many of the people of New Orleans. "We have no right," he declared, "from anything that is known, or from anything that is likely to be discovered, to rank yellow fever as one of the avoidable causes of mortality." Speaking from long years of experience, he wrote of his own treatment: "In yellow fever I have laid aside the lancet; I have dismissed the cuppers and leechers, *in toto*; I allow no hot mustard foot-baths, or body-baths, as there is generally more than enough of heat. I never make an effort by piling bed-clothes on my patient, to force a perspiration. . . ." Blistering and the administration of large doses of quinine were worse than useless, he contended, and he urged that attempts be made to keep the patient cool and comfortable. Then in a sweeping assertion he virtually dismissed the standard therapy for yellow fever: "It is not a disease for blood-letting, cupping, leeching, mercurialization, vesication, antimonials, or rattling cathartics. I tried them well, many years ago, and speak from experience." He concluded his sage observations on the disease by asserting that he was convinced that natives acquire some type of immunity, either at the breast or below the age of five through a mild attack. He recognized, too, that one attack of yellow fever confers immunity for life. [27]

The author of another pamphlet on the epidemic, who simply listed himself as "A Physician of New Orleans," agreed in essence with his colleagues. The disease, he wrote, "baffled the skill of the most scientific and experienced practitioners." Narcotics and large doses of quinine were soon abandoned by "the most judicious physicians," but quinine was still used extensively with "deafness, blindness, swelled limbs, and hopeless insanity being in many cases the final result." Castor oil was generally administered "with comparatively good effect" in the early stages of the disease but proved harmful as the sickness progressed. "Cupping, bleeding, and the use of calomel and blue pill," he continued, "were found to be equally useless, though much employed." In general, he said, it must be confessed that good nursing, a reliance upon the recuperative powers of nature, and "hygienic management . . . saved more lives than medicine." As the failure of the standard forms of medicine became obvious to the better physicians, it became the practice in Charity Hospital, he noted, to give no drugs to entering patients who had been sick for four or more days, and, surprisingly enough, "a large number of these cases recovered." [28]

The same author stated that the homeopathic physicians claimed to have been successful in their treatment, but no full or accurate account of their practice had been made. One of the homeopaths, Dr. A. Cartier, published an article on October 16 in which he asserted that he had treated 175 unacclimated patients and lost only 16—despite the fact that the majority were of the poorer class which suffered the highest casualties.[29] If Dr. Cartier's figures are correct, his 9 percent case fatality rate would have been well below the average, which, according to contemporary observers, was from 20 to 30 percent. Another homeopathic physician, Dr. William H. Holcombe, reported results that were even more successful. Holcombe and another homeopath, Dr. F. A. W. Davis, were practicing in Natchez in 1853 when the yellow fever attacked. The two men treated a total of 555 cases and lost only 33, or approximately 6 percent of them. Holcombe gave a good insight into the infinitesimal dosage of the homeopathic treatment when he mentioned that for severe cases in the second stage of the fever he prescribed 1/10,000 of a grain of silver nitrate dissolved in half a glass of water. Speaking of the regular or allopathic practitioners, he remarked grimly: "The dominant Molochs of allopathy, the lancet, calomel, quinine, and 'expectant medicine,' each had his altar, and each received a satisfactory quota of victims." [30]

Statistics provided by other homeopathic physicians for earlier epidemics tend to substantiate their claims of success in dealing with yellow fever. Their opposition to quinine, mercury, blood-letting, and purging obviously placed them in a favorable position, while the minuteness of their dosages guaranteed that if the medicine was of no benefit to the patient, it would at least do him no harm. Rather ironically, although their reasoning was quite different, by the end of the epidemic of 1853, the allopathic or orthodox physicians and the homeopathic doctors had arrived at essentially the same treatment for yellow fever.

Intelligent laymen soon recognized the value of good nursing and minimal medication. A New Yorker who caught yellow fever in New Orleans declared that the chances of a patient's recovery varied "with the degree of favor his physician enjoys at the shop of the apothecary. If he has a nephew or a cousin in the drug line, the patient is a dead man from the second day"; but if the physician was a student of Hahnemann (the founder of homeopathy) "and be a profound thinker upon medical science, . . . the patient is, probably, a confirmed convalescent the fifth day." A New Orleans newspaperman who served as correspondent for one of the small-town newspapers, reported that those patients who were induced to perspire freely had the best chance for recovery. Any individual, he wrote, who will keep warm and have a good nurse "will come forth well in a few days, and with but little medicine—oil, mustard for baths and plasters, and four or five grains of quinine will suffice." When this treatment was provided "within 12 hours of the first symptoms of fever," he had never seen it fail.[31]

Even in the South where heroic medical practice survived much longer than in the Northeast, the more able physicians were gradually turning away from excessive bleeding, blistering, purging, and dosing by the mid-nineteenth century. The experiences of New Orleans with yellow fever accentuated this trend, and the complete failure of strenuous medicine to cope with yellow fever in 1853 had a profound impact upon southern medical practice. The lessons learned from this epidemic had applicability to the treatment of all diseases. If the best that could be done for a yellow fever patient was to keep him comfortable while the disease ran its course, was it not possible that this treatment might prove best for typhoid, typhus, and the other major fevers, too? Moreover, the disastrous consequences of large doses of mercury and quinine upon yellow fever patients brought into sharp focus both the immediate and long term effects of these dangerous drugs. It would not be correct to credit one epidemic with moderating southern medical practice, for the process was well underway before 1853. Yet the New Orleans physicians had an unprecedented opportunity to observe the results of a wide variety of treatments, and there were indeed few doctors who survived into the fall of 1853 with their faith in traditional methods unshaken.

Both directly and indirectly, the yellow fever epidemic of 1853 made a strong impression on the South. Physicians, nurses, and Howard Association members carried the lessons learned by bitter experience in New Orleans to many other towns and cities. An indirect effect, but possibly an even more important one, arose from the leading role played by New Orleans as the chief medical center for the Southwest. The roster of students in the Medical Department of the University of Louisiana, the forerunner of the present day Tulane University Medical School, shows that the school drew widely from the southern states.

As the slavery crisis was developing in the 1850's and southern nationalism was gaining ascendancy, the argument was set forth that because of climatic and other environmental differences southern medical practice was quite distinct from that of Europe and the northern states. The most articulate of the exponents of this viewpoint was Dr. Samuel Cartwright, who bolstered his thesis by asserting that physiological differences between whites and Negroes further separated southern medicine from that of the North. The main point to these arguments was that southern medical students, many of whom were attending northern medical schools, such as Jefferson Medical College and the University of Pennsylvania in Philadelphia, should be trained in southern schools. As sectional differences grew, the enrollment in the University of Louisiana Medical Department soared, and by 1856 a second medical school was opened in New Orleans.[32] Thus the development of New Orleans as a center for southern medical training helped to assure that the lessons learned from the grim experience of 1853 would leave a major imprint upon southern medical practice.

The many caustic attacks upon the medical profession in general and upon individual physicians specifically should not obscure the real and courageous efforts made by members of the profession. Whatever their opinions, most people eagerly sought medical aid in times of serious illness; and the doctors, handicapped by the limitations of medical knowledge, circumscribed by tradition, and subject as always to the expectations of patients, did their best under the circumstances. During epidemics, the percentage of physicians who fell victim was probably higher than that of any other professional group. Repeatedly in the New Orleans papers brief obituary notices appeared mourning the death of some young physician who had but recently come to the city to work with yellow fever patients. In the towns outside of New Orleans, where yellow fever was a rare visitor, local physicians almost invariably contracted the disorder in the early days of the outbreak, and it is obvious from the tone of their obituaries that the townspeople felt a genuine sense of loss. For example, an item from Mobile read: "MELANCHOLY.—We are deeply grieved to announce the death of Dr.

Thomas G. Randolph, late physician to the Samaritan Society of Mobile, who died of yellow fever about six o'clock on the morning of the 21st inst., after an illness of four days." An account of the death of Dr. Louis Eugene Dufay, who died in St. John the Baptist Parish, stated that, although he had only lately arrived from France, he had volunteered his services to the Howard Association and devoted himself to aiding his "suffering fellow creatures." [33]

As the epidemic had intensified in midsummer and many citizens were fleeing for safety, dozens of young doctors seeking fame and fortune entered New Orleans. Some were confident of their ability to deal with yellow fever; others had doubts but were anxious to test their skill. As the cases mounted with incredible rapidity the Howard Association eagerly hired all available medical men. At one time it had about 300 physicians in either part- or full-time employment. The older New Orleans doctors were immune to the fever, but the newcomers quickly fell sick. The more fortunate ones survived the illness and could then build a permanent practice in New Orleans—unless, of course, they succumbed later to Asiatic cholera, typhoid, or the host of other ailments besetting mankind in the so-called good old days. A short necrology published in the *New Orleans Medical & Surgical Journal* on September 1 shows both the youthfulness of the deceased physicians and their out-of-state origin. Of four doctors listed, one was a native of New York, another of St. Louis, a third of Nashville, and a fourth of Petersburg, Virginia. The oldest was 40 years of age, and the others were in their early twenties. On this same day the *Delta* reported the death of a young Irish physician, a Dr. F. Ryan, a recent arrival who had come to work with yellow fever patients but who had fallen victim to the disease himself.[34]

A Baton Rouge newspaper reported gratefully on September 24 that six nurses and two doctors had just arrived from the Howard Association in New Orleans. The contingent was particularly welcome, the paper added, since two of the town's young physicians were already down with yellow fever. The shortage of acclimated physicians occasionally forced the Howard Association to send newcomers to help fever-stricken areas. A report from St. John the Baptist Parish early in October asserted that not one of the three physicians sent by the Howard Association was available for professional services. One was dangerously ill with yellow fever, and the other two had returned to New Orleans to convalesce from the disease.[35]

The genuine feeling of affection which most physicians engendered in their patients is reflected not only in the obituary columns but also in scattered news items. The *Delta* of New Orleans, which was highly critical of the medical profession generally, noted on August 30 that Dr. Warren Stone, one of the city's outstanding surgeons, had gone to the country for the sake of his health. Instead of criticizing him for deserting his post, it mentioned that he had suffered a heavy bereavement in his family, praised his work, and explained that no one was more deserving of a little recreation. On October 25 the citizens of Jackson, Mississippi, presented a fine horse and buggy to a Dr. Gaulden of New Orleans for his unremitting care during their yellow fever epidemic.[36]

When the editor of the *Boston Medical and Surgical Journal* excoriated the physicians of New Orleans for their ill treatment of patients, Dr. Hester indignantly refuted the charges in his New Orleans journal. "We venture to say our Boston contemporary might learn to judge more justly of the profession in New Orleans, were he to follow them in their god-like labors through an epidemic." He regretted that a respectable medical journal had given publicity to such unfounded charges: "We deserve a better fate than this, after the risk—the toils, and the anxiety through which we have passed." Surely, when the Boston editor realizes that the New Orleans physicians treated 20,000 of the sick poor, Dr. Hester concluded, "he will be a little more merciful to us, who have sinned rather in *forgetting* our own interest, and attending to the health and welfare of those who do not even thank us for sympathy." [37]

The doctor-patient relationship, to be effective, must be founded upon trust and respect, and most physicians sought to merit the approbation of their patients. Even those doctors who rigidly applied current medical theories or who strenuously resorted to traditional therapy did so from a conscientious conviction that they were helping their patients. They blistered and bled themselves when they felt it was necessary and never doubted the efficacy of the treatment. While it was true that some physicians treated the disease and forgot the patient, most were concerned with the sick man as an individual and thus tempered their medicine to suit the individual case. Even for doctors not overly endowed with intelligence, experience and common sense frequently dictated that they moderate their practices. Undoubtedly many abuses in medical practice occurred—and prevailing medical ideas lent themselves to such abuse—yet the individual practitioner was still looked upon as a friend of the family, doing his best with whatever means were available. The public might decry the profession in general, but they tended to respect their personal physician.

CHAPTER XI

The Summing Up

THE DISASTROUS EVENTS OF 1853 present a fine example of how a large city reacted to a major catastrophe. In a period of five months, approximately 40,000 cases of yellow fever developed, and 11,000 citizens lost their lives. Of these deaths, almost 9,000 were definitely attributed to yellow fever—and the toll may have been higher. The population of New Orleans during the busy winter season was estimated to be in excess of 150,000, but this figure included many transient merchants, brokers, riverboatmen, and so forth. During the hot summer months, the middle and upper class citizens ordinarily sent their families out of town, and this normal exodus was greatly augmented in June and July of 1853, first by the rumored presence of yellow fever and later by the confirmation of its existence. The estimates of how many had left the city by the time the epidemic was striking in full force vary widely, ranging from 30,000 to 75,000, but it is probably safe to assume that about 100,000 people remained throughout the summer months. On this basis, New Orleans was literally decimated by the epidemic. For a period of at least two months nearly all economic activity was halted. Caring for the sick and burying the dead was the major occupation of the healthy.

Yellow fever was no stranger to New Orleans, but several years of relative freedom had convinced most citizens that the disease was relaxing its grip. Although in each of the preceding summers the disease had made its appearance, the few hundred cases were considered of little importance. The epidemic of 1853 began quietly and gave little indication of the sword of pestilence which was to menace the city. The disease lurked in the poorer sections on the waterfront throughout June and did not attack with full force until July. Wishful thinking and a desire to avoid disrupting the economy led the civic authorities to refuse both to admit the existence of an epidemic or to take necessary precautions. As the daily total of deaths soared above one hundred, the optimism which had characterized newspaper editorials and official pronouncements rapidly faded; and as the daily death toll climbed above two hundred, an air of disbelief appeared in contemporary writings. When the newspapers reported more than 250 deaths in a single day, the public reaction was one of shocked incredulity.

Yet by the time the peak of the outbreak was reached on August 20, the city's resources were effectively mobilized, and there was no evidence of panic. Municipal authorities and voluntary groups had made ample provision for tending the sick and burying the dead. By the end of August, it was quickly realized that the worst was over, and a spirit of optimism was emerging. Despite the fact that about 740 yellow fever deaths occurred during the first seven days of September, the newspapers, diaries, and personal letters show that the citizens were already looking to the revival of business and a return to normality. The advent of November brought with it a minor Asiatic cholera outbreak, but yellow fever had virtually disappeared. Business was booming and the commercial pulse of New Orleans was once again throbbing. Occasional references were made to the summer just past, but the citizens of New Orleans were looking to their golden future.

To the casual observer, the onward swirl of human events had engulfed the past, and the tide of human affairs was sweeping New Orleans forward. The past may have been prologue, but New Orleans was living in the present, and its citizens had little time for backward glances. They were too busy exchanging mountains of cotton, sugar, and other raw materials for the processed goods of Europe and the North to ponder over what changes the epidemic summer of 1853 had wrought. Nevertheless, New Orleans would never again be the same.

In the field of medicine the slow change which southern practice had been undergoing was given a sudden and sharp impetus. The more able physicians had learned from personal experience and from the writings of leading northern, French, and British medical men that the excessive bleeding, blistering, purging, and vomiting which characterized so much of southern and western medicine was worse than useless. There were still many outstanding doctors, however, who felt they could conquer yellow fever and other serious diseases by drastic measures—large doses of quinine or calomel, bleeding to syncope, and so forth. The disastrous yellow fever epidemic in New Orleans and its widespread impact upon all the Gulf Coast states made it clear to nearly every physician that there was no single answer to yellow fever. Virtually every known form of treatment was tried and, in almost every case, was found wanting. The lesson for all to see in 1853 was that good nursing and minimal medication provided the best hope for yellow fever patients. The two New Orleans medical journals, the only medical publications in the Southwest, carried this message throughout the South.

The yellow fever epidemic of 1853 did not suddenly moderate southern medical practice; rather it hastened the culmination of a trend. The epidemic demonstrated clearly what most physicians were coming to suspect—that excessive medication was not only useless but positively harmful. Nonetheless, in rural areas, and in some towns and cities, strenuous forms of therapy continued for many years. The expectations of patients, an almost totally inadequate system of medical training, and a lack of effective medical licensure laws until the end of the century guaranteed that traditional medical practice would survive into the twentieth century. But southern medical schools and medical journals no longer sought to provide an intellectual basis for the crude, rigorous practices of earlier days.

Of more significance to the development of New Orleans was the impact of the epidemic upon the municipal government. The paternalism practiced by the French and Spanish colonial governments of Louisiana did not survive the American acquisition and the influx of Anglo-Saxons. In England the rise of puritanism, with its emphasis upon thrift, industry, and individualism, had replaced the benevolent despotism of the Tudors; and the government no longer felt much obligation to the deserving poor. American republicanism, which took over Louisiana in 1803, placed a high value upon individual freedom. Most Americans looked upon governmental activity as a restriction upon individual initiative, and they firmly believed that the least government was the best government. The care of the poor and sick was considered properly an area for private charity. While the growth of towns and cities had forced municipal governments into accepting such functions as cleaning streets, removing sewage, and even into taking some responsibility for supplying good water, these activities were undertaken reluctantly—well-to-do citizens were generally opposed to spending their tax money upon the dirty and dissolute poor. It was much simpler and

—they thought—cheaper to ascribe the filthy and festering conditions of the slum areas to the immorality and irresponsibility of the slum tenants.

One way in which the fetish for individual freedom found expression was in opposition to medical licensing. The medical profession in Louisiana, as elsewhere, had sought to raise the standards and qualifications of its members by establishing state or local boards of medical examiners. The public, already suspicious of doctors, looked upon licensing boards as monopolistic devices to enable physicians to prey upon the public. In state legislatures throughout the country, senators and representatives in the 1830's and 1840's fervently fought for the right of every citizen to select his own physician—be he an allopath, a homeopath, a hydropath, an herbalist, or an outright quack. As the movement gained momentum, it swept away nearly all regulations pertaining to medical practice and left a golden harvest for quack doctors.

With this background, it is easy to understand why the Common Council of New Orleans made it a practice to adjourn in July so its members could retreat to the resort areas and thus escape the sickly season. That one or two thousand individuals might die from yellow fever was not the concern of the councilmen. The sick poor were objects of Christian charity, and any municipal officer who felt responsibility for them was free to act as a private citizen. Nonetheless, as yellow fever intensified its attacks upon New Orleans in the 1830's and 1840's, more and more voices were heard demanding that the city fathers take action to prevent or mitigate the worst effects of epidemic diseases. For about five years prior to 1853, men like Dr. E. H. Barton, Dr. J. C. Simonds, and Dr. E. D. Fenner had sought to awaken leading citizens to the enormous annual death rate in the city and to prove to them an intimate relationship between dirt and disease.

Their efforts proved fruitless, however, and sheer tragedy and complete municipal breakdown were only averted because of three factors. First, Mayor A. D. Crossman provided firm leadership and exercised the full power of his office. Secondly, most city employees remained at their posts and were aided by the continued functioning of the finance committee of the City Council. Finally, the belatedly established board of health, working in close cooperation with the mayor, helped tide the city over the crisis. Amazingly, when one considers what conditions must have been like in August with thousands of sick and dying in the city, there was never any real panic. The closest the city came to a breakdown was during the first few days in August when unburied bodies began to pile up at one of the cemeteries. Although hesitant and unsure of his authority at first, Mayor Crossman soon took charge and within two or three days brought this situation under control.

The most striking failure of the city government was in the cowardly action of the councilmen; but far more significant was the way in which the majority of officials remained faithful to their trust and helped the city survive the epidemic. The courage of Mayor Crossman and his cohorts deserves to be remembered; in demonstrating what responsible officials could do, Mayor Crossman helped to create a civic consciousness, a sense of responsibility for the welfare of all people. Henceforth it was assumed in New Orleans that civic officials should take responsibility for the public welfare. This is not to say that they always accepted their responsibilities, but at least they were expected to do so. Private charity continued to play a large role, but increasingly the city and state were moving into the picture. Here again, the epidemic did not bring any startling innovation, but, as with medical practice, it added both impetus and direction to the existing trend.

Although much credit is due Mayor Crossman and his associates, the major share of the task of providing for the victims of the epidemic was assumed by the large number of voluntary groups. The most prominent of these, of course, was the Howard Association. The remarkable work of the Howard members in New Orleans has been fully covered; even more to its credit were the association's efforts against yellow fever in other stricken towns and cities. Finding that the physicians it employed used very diverse forms of therapy, the association wisely permitted the patient to select his doctor if he wished and made no attempt to pass judgment on professional medical matters. Its chief medical contribution was to provide excellent nursing, possibly the most effective of all nineteenth century therapeutic aids.

The generous response to the Howard Association appeals for financial assistance reflects a high level of social consciousness on the part of the American people and a great confidence in the honesty and ability of the association. Moreover, the funds donated to the association represent only a part of the money given to New Orleans. A number of municipalities made contributions directly to the city authorities, and additional funds were given to the many religious, national, fraternal, and other organizations which were actively aiding the members and families of their own particular groups. Only brief reference to these voluntary groups has been made, since their individual efforts were minor compared to those of the city government and the Howard Association, but their combined help was an important factor in the city's survival.

The united efforts of all groups, civic and voluntary, drew a large part of the population into their activities. Individuals of all social classes were kept too busy making tangible contributions to the welfare of the sick to worry about their own danger. The psychological bene- fit from these united endeavors is difficult to assess, but it must have played an important role in enabling the people of New Orleans to face the ever-increasing daily death toll with an amazing calmness and as- surance. The epidemic of 1853 represents the high point of voluntary effort in New Orleans; thereafter municipal and state action was to in- crease in scope. Yet the remarkable success of these endeavors guaran- teed that voluntary organizations would continue to play a large part in American public concerns.

It is impossible to read the New Orleans newspapers and journals in the late fall of 1853 and not be astounded at the way in which the trag- edy of the preceding summer was seemingly disregarded. Trade and commerce were pouring down the Mississippi River, filling the ware- houses with goods and the boardinghouses and hotels with transients. Immigrants from northwestern Europe were crowding the customs offices, some to remain in New Orleans and others to seek their fortunes in the interior. Artisans and professional workers, too, were flocking to the city, hoping to gain rapid wealth. Forests of masts overshadowed the city wharves; the streets were crowded, and amid the bustle and activity of the booming city, it must have been hard to visualize the desolation of only a few months earlier.

The loss of a tenth of its population scarcely seems to have affected the growth and prosperity of New Orleans. Within a few months the influx of newcomers had more than compensated for any losses, and the city continued to participate in the booming prosperity of the 1850's. The resilience of the human kind and its ability to absorb the cruelest blows of fortune were never better illustrated. Whatever be- tides mankind as individuals, the human race flows inexorably on. The biological instinct for survival allows concern only for the present and the future; it permits little time for dwelling on the dead. In any event, New Orleans, in December of 1853, was a thriving, bustling city with what seemed a short past and a great and glorious future. The yellow fever epidemic was over, the people were healthy, and the future would take care of itself.

Notes

CHAPTER I

1 J. C. Simonds, "Report on the Hygienic Characteristics of New Orleans," *Transactions of the American Medical Association*, III (1850), 277–80; Edward H. Barton, *Annual Report of the Board of Health for 1849* (New Orleans, 1849), 13.
2 John Duffy (ed.), *The Rudolph Matas History of Medicine in Louisiana*, (2 vols.; Baton Rouge, 1958), I, chapters 10 and 16; II, chapters 5 and 16.
3 *Cohen's New Orleans Directory for 1853* (New Orleans, 1853), v.
4 *Bee*, May 4, 1853. (In the absence of any city designation, all newspapers cited in notes were published in New Orleans.)
5 *Ibid.*, May 9, 1853.
6 *Ibid.*, May 4, 1853.
7 *Ibid.*
8 *New Orleans Medical & Surgical Journal*, IX (1852–53), 843–44; hereinafter cited as *Medical & Surgical Journal*.
9 *Ibid.*, 697–98.
10 *Ibid.*, 843.
11 *Bee*, May 19, 1853.
12 *Ibid.*
13 *Daily Picayune*, May 29, 1853.
14 E. D. Fenner, *History of the Epidemic of Yellow Fever at New Orleans, La., in 1853* (New York, 1854), 15.
15 *Ibid.*, 15–16.
16 *Ibid.*, 16–18.
17 *Ibid.*, 18–19.
18 *Ibid.*, 21.

CHAPTER II

1 *Bee*, June 1, 1853.
2 *Ibid.*, June 8, 1853.
3 *Ibid.*, June 1, 1853.
4 *Daily Picayune*, June 1, 1853.
5 *Daily Delta*, June 7, 1853.
6 *Ibid.*, June 17, 18, 1853.

7 *Daily Crescent*, June 22, 1853.
8 *Ibid.*, June 24, 1853.
9 *Daily Picayune*, June 28, 1853.
10 *Daily Delta*, June 29, 1853.
11 *Ibid.*, June 30, 1853.
12 *Bee*, June 28, 30, 1853.
13 New Orleans City Council, Board of Assistant Aldermen, *Proceedings*, June 14, 21, 1853.
14 *Bee*, June 15, 1853.
15 New Orleans City Council, Board of Assistant Aldermen, *Proceedings*, June 21, 1853.
16 *Ibid.*
17 *Ibid.*, June 28, 1853.
18 *Bee*, June 29, 30, 1853.
19 *Daily Picayune*, June 23, 1853.
20 *Daily Delta*, June 22, 1853.
21 *Daily Picayune*, June 24, 1853.
22 *Daily Delta*, June 26, 1853.
23 For the history of the New Orleans Board of Health see Duffy (ed.), *Rudolph Matas History*, II, chapters 7 and 17.
24 *New Orleans Monthly Medical Register*, I (1851–52), 94–95; hereinafter cited as *Monthly Medical Register*.
25 *Daily Picayune*, June 28, 1853.
26 *Bee*, June 29, 30, 1853.
27 *Ibid.*, June 21, 22, 23, 1853.
28 New Orleans City Council, *Ordinances, Resolutions and Permanent Orders*, June 23, 1853.
29 New Orleans City Council, Board of Assistant Aldermen, *Proceedings*, June 28, 1853; Board of Aldermen, *Proceedings*, June 28, 1853.
30 *Bee*, June 29, 1853.
31 *Ibid.*, June 30, 1853.
32 *Medical & Surgical Journal*, X (1853–54), 136–37.
33 *Monthly Medical Register*, II (1853–54), 118.
34 *Ibid.*, 110.
35 *Bee*, July 2, 1853.
36 *Ibid.*
37 *Daily Delta*, Supplement, July 3, 1853.
38 *Daily Picayune*, July 3, 1853.
39 *Daily Delta*, July 3, 1853.
40 *Bee*, July 4, 1853.
41 *Ibid.*, July 6, 1853.
42 *Ibid.*
43 *Ibid.*
44 *Daily Crescent*, July 6, 1853.
45 *Bee*, July 7, 1853.
46 *Daily Delta*, July 10, 12, 1853.
47 *Daily Picayune*, July 12, 1853.
48 *Bee*, July 12, 1853.
49 *Daily Crescent*, July 6, 1853.

CHAPTER III

1 *Daily Picayune*, July 13, 14, 1853.
2 [William L. Robinson], *The Diary of a Samaritan* (New York, 1860), 122.

3 *Cohen's New Orleans Directory for 1854* (New Orleans, 1854), xviii–xxx.
4 New Orleans City Council, Board of Assistant Aldermen, *Proceedings*, July 12, 1853.
5 New Orleans City Council, Board of Aldermen, *Proceedings*, July 12, 1853.
6 New Orleans City Council, Board of Assistant Aldermen, *Proceedings*, July 14, 1853.
7 *Ibid.*
8 *Daily Picayune*, July 15, 1853.
9 *Daily Delta*, July 17, 1853.
10 *Bee*, July 14, 1853.
11 *Daily Delta*, July 18, 1853.
12 *Ibid.*, July 17, 1853.
13 *Bee*, July 20, 1853.
14 New Orleans City Council, Board of Aldermen, *Proceedings*, July 19, 1853.
15 New Orleans City Council, Board of Assistant Aldermen, *Proceedings*, July 19, 1853.
16 *Ibid.*
17 *Bee*, July 20, 1853.
18 *Daily Delta*, July 21, 1853.
19 *Daily Crescent*, July 21, 1853; *Daily Picayune*, July 21, 1853; *Daily Delta*, July 20, 1853, quoting the *Commercial Bulletin*, July 19, 1853.
20 *Daily Delta*, July 22, 1853.
21 *Daily Crescent*, July 19, 1853.
22 *Daily Delta*, July 20, 1853.
23 *Le Courrier de la Louisiane*, July 21, 1853.
24 Fenner, *History of Yellow Fever at New Orleans*, 46.
25 *Daily Delta*, July 24–25, 1853; *Bee*, July 23, 1853; New Orleans City Council, Board of Assistant Aldermen, *Proceedings*, July 22, 1853.
26 *Ibid.*
27 *Ibid.*; *Daily Delta*, Supplement, July 24, 1853.
28 New Orleans City Council, Board of Assistant Aldermen, *Proceedings*, July 22, 1853.
29 *Daily Picayune*, July 24, 1853.
30 *Daily Delta*, July 24, 1853.
31 *Bee*, July 26, 1853.
32 *Ibid.*
33 *Ibid.*
34 *Ibid.*, July 27, 1853.
35 *Ibid.*, July 28, 1853.

CHAPTER IV

1 George W. Cable, *The Creoles of Louisiana* (New York, 1884), 298–99.
2 *Le Courrier de la Louisiane*, July 21, 1853, quoted in the *Daily Delta*, July 22, 1853.
3 *Daily Crescent*, July 25, 1853.
4 *Daily Picayune*, July 26, 1853.
5 *Daily Crescent*, July 26, 1853; *Bee*, July 26, 1853.
6 *Daily Delta*, July 29, 1853; "The Plague in the South-West," *DeBow's Review*, XV (1853), 615.
7 *Bee*, July 28, 1853.
8 *Daily Delta*, July 26, 1853.
9 For a complete account of Dr. McFarlane's theory see *DeBow's Review*, XVI (1854), 463–66.

10 J. S. McFarlane, *The Epidemic Summer: List of Interments in all Cemeteries in New Orleans* . . . (New Orleans, 1853), v.
11 *Daily Delta*, July 26, 1853.
12 *Ibid.*, August 11, 1853.
13 *Bee*, July 27, 1853.
14 *Daily Delta*, July 29, 31, 1853.
15 *Ibid.*
16 *Ibid.*
17 *Ibid.*
18 *Ibid.*; *Bee*, July 27, 1853.
19 *Daily Crescent*, July 27, 1853.
20 *Daily Picayune*, July 26, 1853.
21 *Bee*, July 27, 1853.
22 *Daily Delta*, July 25, 1853.
23 *Ibid.*, July 27, 1853.
24 *Ibid.*
25 *Bee*, July 29, 1853.
26 *Daily Picayune*, July 30, 1853.
27 *Daily Delta*, July 30, 1853.
28 For information on the Charity Hospital see Duffy (ed.), *Rudolph Matas History*, II, 198–236.
29 [Robinson], *Diary of a Samaritan*, 123–24.
30 *Ibid.*, 126–27.
31 *Ibid.*, 130–31.
32 *Ibid.*, 131.
33 John Duffy (ed.), *Parson Clapp of the Stranger's Church of New Orleans* (Baton Rouge, 1957).
34 Theodore Clapp, *Autobiographical Sketches and Recollections during a Thirty-Five Years' Residence in New Orleans* (2nd ed.; Boston, 1858), 189.
35 *Ibid.*
36 *Bee*, July 30, 1853.
37 *Daily Delta*, July 31, 1853.

CHAPTER V

1 *Monthly Medical Register*, II (1852–53), 130.
2 *Daily Delta*, August 1, 1853.
3 *Bee*, August 1, 1853.
4 Fenner, *History of Yellow Fever at New Orleans*, 38.
5 *Bee*, August 3, 1853.
6 *Ibid.*
7 *Daily Delta*, August 3, 1853.
8 *Daily Crescent*, August 8, 1853.
9 *Bee*, August 4, 1853.
10 *Ibid.*
11 *Ibid.*, August 8, 1853.
12 *Monthly Medical Register*, II (1852–53), 131.
13 *Daily Crescent*, August 3, 1853.
14 *Daily Delta*, August 3, 1853.
15 *Ibid.*
16 *Ibid.*
17 *Daily Picayune*, August 7, 8, 1853.
18 *Daily Delta*, August 8, 1853.

19 *Daily Picayune*, August 8, 1853.
20 *Daily Delta*, August 9, 1853.
21 *Ibid.*
22 *Ibid.*
23 *Ibid.*
24 *Daily Crescent*, August 11, 1853.
25 *Ibid.*
26 *Ibid.*
27 *Ibid.*, August 9, 1853.
28 *Daily Delta*, August 9, 1853.
29 Fenner, *History of Yellow Fever at New Orleans*, 38.
30 *Daily Delta*, August 11, 1853.
31 *Ibid.*, August 11, 14, 1853.
32 *Ibid.*, August 11, 1853.
33 *Ibid.*
34 *Bee*, August 15, 1853.
35 *Ibid.*, August 19, 1853.
36 *Daily Picayune*, August 19, 1853.
37 *Bee*, August 19, 1853.
38 "The Plague in the South-West," *DeBow's Review*, XV (1853), 626.

CHAPTER VI

1 [?], *History of the Yellow Fever in New Orleans, During the Summer of 1853 ...By a Physician of New Orleans, ...* (Philadelphia and St. Louis, 1854), 22–23.
2 *Bee*, August 20, 1853.
3 *Price-Current*, August 20, 1853; *Daily Delta*, August 20, 1853.
4 *Daily Delta*, August 21, 1853.
5 *Ibid.*
6 *Daily Picayune*, August 21, 1853.
7 *Daily Delta*, August 21, 1853.
8 *Bee*, August 20, 1853.
9 *Daily Picayune*, August 19, 1853.
10 *Daily Delta*, August 27, 1853.
11 *Daily Crescent*, August 23, 1853.
12 *Bee*, August 22, 1853.
13 *Daily Picayune*, August 16, 18, 1853; *Daily Delta*, August 19, 1853.
14 [?], *History of Yellow Fever in New Orleans*, 22.
15 *Daily Delta*, August 19, 1853.
16 *Bee*, August 22, 23, 1853.
17 *Daily Delta*, August 23, 1853.
18 *Ibid.*
19 *Bee*, August 23, 1853.
20 *Daily Delta*, August 24, 1853; *Daily Crescent*, August 25, 1853.
21 *Bee*, August 27, 1853; *Price-Current*, August 27, 1853.
22 *Bee*, August 29, 1853.
23 [?], *History of Yellow Fever in New Orleans*, 29.
24 *Bee*, August 29, 1853.
25 *Daily Delta*, August 24, 1853.
26 *Ibid.*, August 25, 1853.
27 *Bee*, August 23, 1853; *Daily Delta*, August 25, 1853.
28 *Daily Delta*, August 25, 1853; *Bee*, August 27, 1853.

29 *Bee*, August 27, 1853; *Delta Delta*, August 28, 1853; *Daily Picayune*, August 31, 1853.
30 *Daily Delta*, August 27, 1853; *Daily Picayune*, August 31, 1853.
31 *Daily Picayune*, August 29, 1853; *Bee*, August 30, 1853.
32 *Daily Picayune*, August 31, 1853.
33 Quoted in *Daily Delta*, August 31, 1853; *Bee*, August 29, 1853.
34 *Daily Crescent*, August 12, 1853.
35 *Daily Picayune*, August 24, 1853; *Daily Delta*, August 24, 1853.
36 *Daily Delta*, August 24, 1853.
37 *Daily Picayune*, August 31, 1853.
38 *Daily Delta*, September 2, 3, 1853.
39 *Daily Picayune*, August 31, 1853.
40 *Daily Delta*, August 16, 24, 1853.
41 *Ibid.*, August 27, 30, September 4, 1853.
42 *Ibid.*, August 17, 1853; *Daily Picayune*, August 18, 1853.
43 *Daily Delta*, August 18, 1853.
44 *Bee*, August 24, 1853.
45 *Daily Crescent*, August 18, 1853.
46 Quoted in the *Daily Delta*, August 26, 1853.

CHAPTER VII

1 *Medical & Surgical Journal*, X (1853–54), 278.
2 *Bee*, September 1, 1853.
3 *Daily Picayune*, September 2, 1853; *Price-Current*, September 1, 1853.
4 *Daily Delta*, September 1, 3, 1853.
5 *Ibid.*, August 26, 30, September 1, 1853.
6 *Ibid.*, September 1, 1853.
7 *Ibid.*, August 28, September 6, 1853.
8 *Ibid.*, September 4, 6, 8, 9, 1853; *Daily Picayune*, September 8, 1853.
9 *Daily Delta*, September 4, 1853.
10 *Bee*, September 5, 1853.
11 *Daily Crescent*, September 6, 1853; *Daily Delta*, September 7, 11, 1853.
12 *Daily Picayune*, September 11, 1853; *Bee*, September 13, 1853.
13 *Daily Delta*, September 13, 1853.
14 *Ibid.*, September 16, 1853.
15 *Bee*, September 19, 26, 1853; *Daily Crescent*, September 26, 1853.
16 *Daily Delta*, September 27, 28, October 4, 1853; *Bee*, September 26, 1853.
17 *Daily Delta*, September 29, 1853.
18 *Daily Picayune*, September 29, 1853; *Daily Crescent*, September 30, 1853; *Bee*, September 29, 1853.
19 *Price-Current*, October 1, 1853.
20 *Bee*, October 3, 1853; *Daily Crescent*, October 6, 1853.
21 *Price-Current*, October 8, 1853; *Daily Picayune*, October 8, 1853; *Daily Delta*, October 6, 8, 1853; *Bee*, October 8, 24, 28, 1853; *Daily Crescent*, October 24, 1853.
22 *Daily Delta*, October 11, 13, 1853; *Bee*, October 11, 1853; Duffy (ed.), *Parson Clapp*, 45–46.
23 *Daily Delta*, October 13, 1853.
24 *Bee*, October 13, 14, 1853; *Daily Picayune*, October 13, 1853; *Daily Crescent*, October 14, 1853.
25 *Daily Crescent*, October 19, 1853; *Price-Current*, October 22, 1853.
26 *Daily Picayune*, October 23, 1853.

27 *Bee*, October 24, 25, 1853.
28 *Daily Picayune*, October 26, 1853.
29 *Price-Current*, October 19, 22, 26, 29, November 2, 5, 16, 1853.
30 *Bee*, November 2, 4, 5, 1853.
31 *Ibid.*, November 7, 10, 14, 1853.
32 *Ibid.*, November 11, 21, 1853.
33 *Daily Delta*, November 19, 1853.
34 *Ibid.*, November 25, 1853.
35 *Bee*, December 12, 1853; *Medical & Surgical Journal*, X (1853–54), 565.

CHAPTER VIII
1 Baton Rouge (La.) *Daily Comet*, August 24, 25, 1853.
2 Vidalia (La.) *Concordia Intelligencer*, August 27, 1853.
3 Baton Rouge (La.) *Daily Comet*, August 12, 1853; Franklin (La.) *Planters' Banner*, August 18, 1853.
4 Franklin (La.) *Planters' Banner*, August 18, 1853.
5 *Ibid.*, September 1, 1853.
6 *Bee*, August 24, 1853.
7 *Daily Delta*, August 14, September 6, 1853.
8 Baton Rouge (La.) *Daily Comet*, August 30, September 1, 6, 1853.
9 *Ibid.*, September 8, 16, 1853.
10 *Daily Delta*, September 27, 1853; Baton Rouge (La.) *Daily Comet*, September 24, October 1, 1853.
11 Baton Rouge (La.) *Daily Comet*, October 4, 19, 1853.
12 *Ibid.*, October 19, 20, November 5, 1853; Baton Rouge (La.) *Advocate*, quoted in *Bee*, November 1, 1853.
13 Alexandria (La.) *Red River Republican*, September 10, 1853; Plaquemine (La.) *Southern Sentinel*, September 10, 1853.
14 Plaquemine (La.) *Southern Sentinel*, September 10, 1853.
15 Opelousas (La.) *Courier*, September 24, 1853; *Daily Delta*, September 15, 1853; *Bee*, September 15, 1853.
16 Opelousas (La.) *Courier*, September 3, 1853.
17 *Ibid.*, September 17, 1853; Franklin (La.) *Planters' Banner*, September 29, 1853.
18 Opelousas (La.) *Courier*, October 1, 1853.
19 *Ibid.*, October 8, 1853.
20 *Ibid.*, November 19, December 10, 31, 1853.
21 *Ibid.*, September 24, 1853.
22 Mobile (Ala.) *Advertiser*, quoted in *Bee*, September 20, 1853; *Bee*, September 1, 1853; Mobile (Ala.) *Tribune*, quoted in *Bee*, September 13, 1853.
23 *Bee*, September 24, 1853.
24 *Daily Delta*, November 1, 1853; *Bee*, September 6, 1853.
25 *Report of the Howard Association of New Orleans: The Epidemic of 1853* (New Orleans, 1853), 3, 25.
26 *Ibid.*, 23–24.

CHAPTER IX
1 *Bee*, September 16, 1853.
2 *Daily Picayune*, September 14, 25, 1853.
3 *Bee*, September 27, 1853; Duffy (ed.), *Rudolph Matas History*, II, chapter 1.
4 *Daily Delta*, September 30, 1853.

5 *Daily Crescent*, October 4, 1853.

6 *Daily Delta*, October 6, 1853; *Daily Picayune*, October 9, 1853.

7 *Report of the Sanitary Commission of New Orleans on the Epidemic of Yellow Fever of 1853* . . . (New Orleans, 1854), iii–v; *Daily Picayune*, October 9, 1853.

8 *Daily Delta*, October 19, 1853; *Daily Picayune*, October 20, 1853.

9 *Daily Picayune*, October 25, 29, 1853.

10 *Commercial Bulletin*, November 1, 1853; *Daily Delta*, Supplement, November 2, 1853.

11 *Daily Picayune*, November 20, 1853; *Bee*, November 23, 1853; *Daily Crescent*, November 25, 1853.

12 *Bee*, December 1, 1853; *Daily Picayune*, December 13, 25, 1853.

13 *Bee*, December 22, 1853.

14 *Daily Picayune*, January 20, 1854; Louisiana State Legislature, *Majority Report of the Joint Committee on Public Health* (New Orleans, 1854).

15 Louisiana State Legislature, *Counter* (Minority) *Report of the Joint Committee on Public Health* (New Orleans, 1854).

16 *Report of the Sanitary Commission of New Orleans*, iii–v, 452–53, 515; *Daily Picayune*, March 9, 1854.

17 *Daily Picayune*, March 14, 18, 1854.

18 *Medical & Surgical Journal*, X (1853–54), 706.

19 Thomas K. Wharton Diary, April 25, 1854, microfilm, Howard-Tilton Memorial Library Archives.

20 For a detailed discussion of these events, see the May, June and July issues of the *Daily Picayune* and other New Orleans newspapers.

21 Wharton Diary, September 21, 26, 1854.

22 *Daily Delta*, August 1, 2, 1853.

23 *Daily Crescent*, August 2, 1853.

24 *Daily Delta*, August 6, 1853; *Commercial Bulletin*, July 12, 1853, quoted in *DeBow's Review*, XV (1853), 600–601.

25 *DeBow's Review*, XVI (1854), 463–64; McFarlane, *The Epidemic Summer*, xi, xii.

26 E. D. Fenner, "The Yellow Fever Quarantine at New Orleans," *Transactions of the American Medical Association*, II (1849), 625–26; Fenner, *History of Yellow Fever at New Orleans*, 73, 76–77.

27 M. Morton Dowler, "Review of the 'Report of the Sanitary Commission of New Orleans on the Epidemic of Yellow Fever of 1853'," *Medical & Surgical Journal*, XI (1854–55), 525–27.

28 M. Morton Dowler, "On the Reputed Causes of Yellow Fever and the So-Called Sanitary Measures of the Day," *Medical & Surgical Journal*, XI (1854–55), 43, 53, 58, 424–25.

29 Samuel A. Cartwright, "On the Prevention of Yellow Fever," *Medical & Surgical Journal*, X (1853–54), 305–306, 312–13, 315–16.

30 *Daily Delta*, August 14, 1853, October 2, 1853.

31 "An Act to Establish Quarantine for the Protection of the State," *Acts Passed by the Second Legislature of the State of Louisiana, Session of 1855* (New Orleans, 1855), Act 336, pp. 471–77.

CHAPTER X

1 *Monthly Medical Register*, II (1853–54), 137.

2 *Daily Delta*, September 1, 1853.

3 *Bee*, September 17, 1853.

4 *Medical & Surgical Journal*, X (1853–54), 401.
5 *Ibid.*, 402.
6 *Ibid.*, 402–403; *Daily Delta*, September 9, 1853.
7 For a complete discussion of this subject see John Duffy, "Sectional Conflict and Medical Education in Louisiana," *Journal of Southern History*, XXIII (1957), 289–306.
8 For a description of medicine in the South see John Duffy, "Medical Practices in the Ante Bellum South," *Journal of Southern History*, XXV (1959), 53–72.
9 Dagobert D. Runes (ed.), *The Selected Writings of Benjamin Rush* (New York, 1947), 143; Richard H. Shryock, *Medicine and Society in America, 1660–1860* (New York, 1960), 67–72.
10 See Duffy, "Medical Practices in the South"; Duffy (ed.), *Rudolph Matas History*, I, 271–73.
11 M. L. Haynie, "Observations on the Fever of Tropical Climates, and the Use of Mercury as a Remedy," *Medical Repository*, N.S., I (1813), 218.
12 *Daily Crescent*, August 17, 23, 24, 1853.
13 *Daily Delta*, August 24, 1853.
14 *Ibid.*, September 3, 11, 1853.
15 *Ibid.*, October 2, 1853.
16 *Ibid.*, September 4, 1853.
17 [Robinson], *Diary of a Samaritan*, 77.
18 *Ibid.*, 132–34.
19 *Medical & Surgical Journal*, X (1853–54), 227–28, 278.
20 *Ibid.*, 279, 352, 403–404.
21 *Ibid.*, 404–405.
22 *Ibid.*, 249.
23 *Daily Delta*, October 20, 1853.
24 McFarlane, *The Epidemic Summer*, vii.
25 Fenner, *History of Yellow Fever at New Orleans*, 57–58, 61.
26 McFarlane, *The Epidemic Summer*, vii.
27 Dowler, "On the Reputed Causes of Yellow Fever," 58; M. Morton Dowler, "Letter on Yellow Fever," *Medical & Surgical Journal*, XI (1854–55), 368–71, 378.
28 [?], *History of Yellow Fever in New Orleans*, 40–41.
29 *Daily Picayune*, October 16, 1853.
30 William H. Holcombe, *Yellow Fever and Its Homeopathic Treatment* (New York, 1856, 31–41.
31 A. O. Hall, *The Manhattaner in New Orleans* (New York and New Orleans, 1857), 69–70; Vidalia (La.) *Concordia Intelligencer*, October 1, 1853.
32 Duffy, "Sectional Conflict and Medical Education," 289–306.
33 *Bee*, September 24, October 15, 1853.
34 *Medical & Surgical Journal*, X (1853–54), 279; *Daily Delta*, September 1, 1853.
35 Baton Rouge (La.) *Daily Comet*, September 24, 1853; *Bee*, October 13, 1853.
36 *Daily Delta*, August 30, November 2, 1853.
37 *Medical & Surgical Journal*, X (1853–54), 386–87.

Bibliography

OFFICIAL RECORDS

The New Orleans yellow fever epidemic of 1853 was reported in detail, and a wealth of source material is available. The New Orleans Public Library has the Proceedings of the Board of Aldermen, the Proceedings of the Board of Assistant Aldermen, and the Ordinances, Resolutions and Permanent Orders of the City Council. In addition to these original manuscript proceedings, one can find scrapbooks in which are posted clippings from the daily newspapers of the official published reports of the City Council meetings. Also in the New Orleans Public Library can be found the Proceedings of the City Council of Carrollton, December 1, 1852, to January 9, 1861.

NEWSPAPERS

The city was well supplied with newspapers, nearly all of which managed to operate throughout the months of crisis. The New Orleans Public Library has a remarkable collection of city papers, and any gaps can be filled in by the holdings of the Louisiana State Library. For the state at large, the finest collection is located in the Louisiana State University Library at Baton Rouge. The most useful New Orleans newspapers were the *Daily Picayune, Daily Crescent, Daily Delta*, the *Bee* (*L'Abeille* in the French edition), the *Louisiana Courier* (*Le Courrier de la Louisiane* in the French edition), and the *Price-Current*.

For the towns outside of New Orleans, the following journals were of value: the *Advocate* (Baton Rouge), the *Concordia Intelligencer* (Vidalia), the *Daily Comet* (Baton Rouge), the *Planters' Banner* (Franklin), *Red River Republican* (Alexandria), *Southern Sentinel* (Plaquemine) and the *Courier* (Opelousas).

Among the official state legislative publications can be found a most intriguing report, the *Majority Report of the Joint Committee on Public Health* (New Orleans, 1854). This study, which was issued in conjunction with the

183

Counter Report of the Joint Committee on Public Health, the minority group, was published as a pamphlet and can also be found in the official records. It contains an account of the epidemic and gives various suggestions as to its cause. In connection with the 1855 act creating the State Board of Health, the *Acts Passed by the Second Legislature of the State of Louisiana, Session of 1855* (New Orleans, 1855), was used.

PAMPHLETS AND REPORTS

Almost as soon as the epidemic ceased, accounts of it began appearing in magazines and in pamphlet form. The authors of most of these reports were well-known medical writers, and, however much they differed as to the cause of the outbreak, their descriptions of conditions in New Orleans are both accurate and graphic. One of the best of these was E. D. Fenner, *History of the Epidemic of Yellow Fever at New Orleans, La., in 1853* (New York, 1854). Two other good pamphlets are J. S. McFarlane, *The Epidemic Summer: List of Interments in all Cemeteries in New Orleans* (New Orleans, 1853); and [?], *History of the Yellow Fever in New Orleans, During the Summer of 1853 . . . By a Physician of New Orleans* (Philadelphia and St. Louis, 1854).

Possibly the most complete account of the outbreak can be found in the *Report of the Sanitary Commission of New Orleans on the Epidemic Yellow Fever of 1853* (New Orleans, 1854). Its chief author was Dr. Edward Barton, but there were contributions by other members of the commission. At the close of its work, the Howard Association issued a complete account of its activities entitled, *Report of the Howard Association of New Orleans, The Epidemic of 1853* (New Orleans, 1853).

MISCELLANEOUS

Two books which describe New Orleans' epidemics in general but have especial applicability to the outbreak of 1853 are Theodore Clapp, *Autobiographical Sketches and Recollections During a Thirty-Five Years' Residence in New Orleans* (2nd ed.; Boston, 1858), and [William L. Robinson], *The Diary of a Samaritan* (New York, 1860). Robinson was a member of the Howard Association, and he describes in detail his work during the summer of 1853. A pamphlet by William H. Holcombe, *Yellow Fever and Its Homeopathic Treatment* (New York, 1856), gives a good account of homeopathic therapy. Among the many personal diaries which were checked, the only one cited was the Thomas K. Wharton Diary, 1853-54, microfilm, Howard-Tilton Memorial Library.

Cohen's New Orleans Directory for 1853 (New Orleans, 1853), and his *Directory* for 1854 were particularly useful. The directories contain, among other valuable information, brief biographical sketches of leading citizens, and short histories of churches and various civic organizations. Two other helpful works were A. O. Hall, *The Manhattaner in New Orleans* (New York and New Orleans, 1857), and George W. Cable, *The Creoles of Loui-*

siana (New York, 1884). *Harper's Magazine* and other national journals published accounts of the epidemic, but the best ones are to be found in J. D. B. DeBow, *The Commercial Review of the South and the West* (1853–54), volumes 15 and 16.

CONTEMPORARY MEDICAL JOURNALS

New Orleans had two medical publications in 1853, the *New Orleans Medical & Surgical Journal* and the *New Orleans Monthly Medical Register*. Both of them continued to publish during the epidemic, and their editorials and articles provide a gold mine of information. Among the miscellaneous articles in medical publications which were helpful are the following: D. W. Brickell, "Biographical Sketch of E. D. Fenner," *Southern Journal of the Medical Sciences*, I (1866), 412–13; E. D. Fenner, "The Yellow Fever Quarantine at New Orleans," *Transactions of the American Medical Association*, II (1849), 625; J. C. Simonds, "Report on the Hygienic Characteristics of New Orleans," *Transactions of the American Medical Association*, III (1850), 277–80; and M. L. Haynie, "Observations on the Fever of Tropical Climates, and the Use of Mercury as a Remedy," *Medical Repository*, N.S., I (1813), 218.

SECONDARY WORKS

Because of the large amount of primary source material available, little resort was made to secondary works. The best account of American medical theory and practice for the early nineteenth century can be found in Richard H. Shryock's *Medicine and Society in America, 1660–1860* (New York, 1960). For Louisiana medicine, the standard work is John Duffy, ed., *The Rudolph Matas History of Medicine in Louisiana* (2 vols.; Baton Rouge, 1958–62). Duffy is also the editor of *Parson Clapp of the Strangers' Church of New Orleans* (Baton Rouge, 1957), which gives a good brief account of Dr. Clapp's life and work. Dagobert D. Runes, ed., *The Selected Writings of Benjamin Rush* (New York, 1947) was also used.

The *Louisiana Historical Quarterly*, which published a great deal of source material in its early history, has a brief account of the 1853 epidemic in Karl J. R. Arndt, "A Bavarian's Journey to New Orleans and Nacogdoches in 1853–1854," *Louisiana Historical Quarterly*, XXIII (1940–41), 1 ff. A valuable essay to be found in the *Journal of Southern History* is Jo Ann Carrigan, "Yellow Fever in New Orleans: Abstractions and Realities," XXV (August, 1959), 339–55. Two other useful articles are John Duffy, "Medical Practices in the Ante Bellum South," *Journal of Southern History*, XXV (1959), 53–72, and Duffy, "Sectional Conflict and Medical Education in Louisiana," *Journal of Southern History*, XXIII (1957), 289–306.

Index